The MAILBOX®

The Education Center®

20-Minute Science

MW00634290

More than **150** of the best ideas and reproducibles from our popular Investigating Science series

Updated for today's teachers and classrooms!

- **Practical activities**
- **Easy-to-do experiments**
- **Meaningful practice pages**
- **Engaging student booklets**

- **Timesaving patterns**
- **Songs that teach**

Science in 20 minutes or less!

Managing Editor: Kelly Robertson

Editorial Team: Becky S. Andrews, Diane Badden, Kimberley Bruck, Karen A. Brudnak, Pam Crane, Chris Curry, Tazmen Hansen, Marsha Heim, Lori Z. Henry, Kitty Lowrance, Mark Rainey, Greg D. Rieves, Hope Rodgers-Medina, Rebecca Saunders, Donna K. Teal, Sharon M. Tresino, Zane Williard

www.themailbox.com

©2012 The Mailbox® Books
All rights reserved.
ISBN 978-1-61276-219-7

Printed in the United States
10 9 8 7 6 5 4 3 2

HPS254880

Table of Contents

20-Minute Science • ©The Mailbox® Books • TEC61364

What's Inside

A Year's Worth of 20-Minute Science!

Timesaving Formats!

- Material lists
- Step-by-step directions
- Quick-to-read descriptions
- Helpful illustrations

Mammals

Must Be a Mammal!

Materials for each student:
copy of page 10

Review the characteristics of mammals with students. Then direct students to mark an X in each box that corresponds to a characteristic of that animal. Inform students that if an animal has all four characteristics, it must be a mammal. Then invite volunteers to name the mammals on the page.

Animal Habitats

Lead students in singing the song shown. Then list the five habitats on the board. Have students name other animals that might live in each habitat as you list their responses under the corresponding headings.

What's a Habitat?
(sung to the tune of "Are You Sleeping?")

What's a habitat? What's a habitat?
Do you know? Do you know?
It's a place where animals naturally find space
To live and grow, to live and grow.

The ocean is a habitat. The ocean is a habitat.
Home for whom? Home for whom?
Walruses and seals, dolphins and whales
Are a few, are a few.

The grassland is a habitat. The grassland is a habitat.
Home for whom? Home for whom?
Elephants and zebras, lions and hyenas
Are a few, are a few.

The woodland is a habitat. The woodland is a habitat.
Home for whom? Home for whom?
Opossums and deer, bobcats and skunks
Are a few, are a few.

The rain forest is a habitat. The rain forest is a habitat.
Home for whom? Home for whom?
Monkeys and sloths, jaguars and toucans
Are a few, are a few.

Life Science

Hungry Mammals

Materials for every two students:
copy of page 11
access to reference materials

10-5-15

Day 1: Review with students the terms *carnivore, herbivore, insectivore,* and *omnivore.* Help students brainstorm examples of each of these types of mammals as you list their answers on the board. (See the list shown.)

Day 2: Review the list of mammals with students. Invite volunteers to name food(s) each mammal might eat. Then direct each pair of students to use the reference materials to complete page 11.

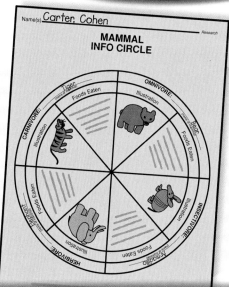

Name(s) Carter, Cohen
Research
MAMMAL
INFO CIRCLE

Herbivores	Carnivores	Omnivores	Insectivores
elephants	tigers	bears	shrews
giraffes	lions	raccoons	hedgehogs
beavers	wolves	humans	moles

Baby Animal Riddle

I live in the farm yard
habitat, or where it lives

I look like fluffy balls of cotton.

I eat grass.

When I am a baby, I am called a lamb

I am a sheep.

What Am I?

Materials for each student:
9" x 12" sheet of construction paper
copy of the riddle pattern from page 12

Display a list of adult mammals on the board. For each mammal, ask a student volunteer to write the corresponding baby name. Then invite each child to choose a mammal and complete the riddle pattern. Direct him to fold his construction paper in half and glue his riddle to the front, as shown. Next, have him open his construction paper and write the mammal's name inside. Invite each child, in turn, to share his riddle and have his classmates guess the mammal he is describing.

Mammal Names	
Adult	**Baby**
bear	cub
deer	fawn
elephant	calf
kangaroo	joey
leopard	cub
beaver	kit

Mammal Names	
Adult	**Baby**
goat	kid
pig	piglet
fox	pup
whale	calf
coyote	pup
sheep	lamb

Life Science

10-5-16

Home, Sweet Home

Materials for every two students:
copy of page 13
access to reference materials

For each mammal on the chart, direct student pairs to make a checkmark in one or more boxes to show which type of home(s) it builds. Have students use the reference materials as needed. When each pair is finished, review the correct answers with students, encouraging them to change any wrong answers.

Names Taylor
Monica

Identifying woodland homes

Home, Sweet Home

Make a ✓ in each box that shows that mammal's home(s).

	Wooded Area	Den	Nest	Burrow	Tunnel	Hollow Tree	Lodge
Bear		✓					
Porcupine							
Skunk		✓		✓		✓	
Fox		✓		✓		✓	
Squirrel			✓	✓		✓	
Chipmunk			✓			✓	
Rabbit					✓		
Marmot				✓			
Woodchuck		✓		✓	✓		
Mole				✓	✓		
Mouse	✓			✓			
Deer	✓			✓		✓	
Beaver							
Opossum		✓					✓
Raccoon	✓	✓				✓	
Marten						✓	
Otter		✓		✓		✓	
Muskrat				✓			

Which Rain Forest?

Materials for each student:
copy of page 14
12" x 18" sheet of construction paper

Remind students that there are three main rain forests in the world: African, Asian, and South American. Also remind them that all rain forests have hot, humid climates due to their close proximity to the equator. Then direct each child to divide his paper into three equal sections and label each section as shown. Next, have each child cut apart the mammal cards and use the code to help him glue each card under the correct heading.

African rain forest	Asian rain forest	South American rain forest
★ chimpanzee ★ ★ okapi ★	▲ Malayan tapir ▲ ▲ Philippine tarsier ▲	● jaguar ● ● kinkajou ●
★ pangolin ★	▲ Sumatran tiger ▲	● giant armadillo ●

Did You Know?
Over half of the world's plant and animal species are found in the rain forests.

See the rain forest animals skill sheet on page 15.

Life Science

Grassland Field Guide

Materials for each student:
copy of pages 16 and 17
booklet with eight 6" x 9" pages and a 9" x 12" construction
   paper cover

Steps:
1. Remind students that a grassland is an area too wet to be a desert but too dry for trees to grow in. Point out areas of grassland on a map or globe.
2. Have each child cut out the cards on pages 16 and 17. Then read each description card aloud and ask each child to color the mammal that is being described.
3. Direct each student to pair the description cards with their corresponding mammal cards. Have her glue each pair on a separate page of her booklet.
4. Have each student title her booklet "Grassland Mammal Field Guide."

Bison
(Prairie)
I am also called the American buffalo. I'm the largest American animal. I have a large hump on my back and hair that forms a beard under my chin. I'm brownish black on most of my body except for my hind part which is just brown.

Burrowing Prairie Mammals

prairie dog
black-footed ferret
striped skunk
spotted skunk
northern pocket gopher
thirteen-lined ground squirrel
meadow vole
American badger
deer mouse
eastern cottontail

Prairie Basement

Materials for each student:
copy of page 18
access to reference materials

Day 1: Share with students prairie mammals that make their homes underground (see the list). Invite each child to choose a burrowing mammal from the list. Then have him use the provided reference materials to research his mammal.

Day 2: Encourage each child to review his research. Then have him complete a copy of page 18.

Did You Know?
Burrowing prairie mammals make their homes underground to protect themselves from predators, the summer heat, and harsh winter storms.

Life Science

Beat the Heat

Materials for each student:
copy of page 19

Review with students how some desert mammals keep cool in their harsh environment. Then have each student cut out the mammal cards on his copy of page 19. Instruct students to listen as you read the first stanza of the poem shown. After reading the stanza, direct each child to find the ground squirrel cutout and glue it to the appropriate box. Continue with the remaining five stanzas of the poem.

"I'd rather not be so hot," said Cape Ground Squirrel.
She stopped in the trail and fluffed her tail and provided her very own shade.

"I'd rather not be so hot," said Desert Bat.
He flew into a cave and slept through the day and waited till dark to come out.

"I'd rather not be so hot," said Collared Peccary.
She and her family, under the mesquite tree, lazed through the hottest hours.

"I'd rather not be so hot," said Fennec Fox.
He dug a big hole and called it a burrow and slept underneath the ground.

"I'd rather not be so hot," said Jackrabbit.
She made a nice fur-lined nest in a patch of cactus and slept the day away.

"I'd rather not be so hot," said Coyote.
He made his underground burrow near a cavern and settled down for the day.

Surviving the Sun

Plan to complete this outdoor experiment on a hot, sunny day to help students understand why most desert animals spend the hottest part of the day away from direct sunlight.

Materials:

3 thermometers
gardener's trowel

resealable plastic bag
3 colored craft sticks

Steps:

1. Take students outside and direct a volunteer to dig a hole about 12 inches deep. Place a thermometer inside the bag, seal it, and then place the bag in the hole.
2. Have a child refill the hole with dirt and then mark the spot with a craft stick.
3. Place a second thermometer in a low-traffic area in direct sunlight. Mark the spot with a craft stick.
4. Place the third thermometer in a low-traffic shady area. Mark the spot with a craft stick.
5. After about 20 minutes, have one student carefully dig up the buried thermometer and read its temperature. Then have additional students read the temperatures on the other thermometers.
6. Compare the temperatures and lead students to realize that the cooler temperatures underground help desert mammals escape the heat.

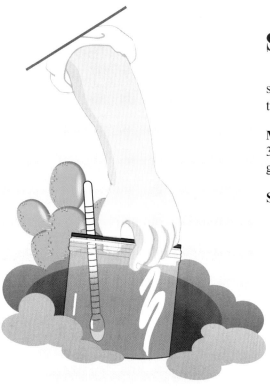

Life Science

Mammals

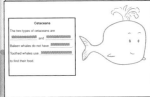

Ocean Mammals

Materials for each student:
copy of page 20
booklet with four 6" x 9" pages and a 9" x 12"
    construction paper cover trimmed to resemble waves
    (staple booklet along the bottom)

Day 1: Use this booklet project to help students learn about the four types of marine mammals. Share with students background information about cetaceans, pinnipeds, sirenians, and sea otters. Lead students in filling in the missing information on page 20.

Day 2: Review the marine animal information. Then have each child cut apart the title card and fact cards from page 20. Have him glue the title card to the cover and each fact card to a different page. Then direct each child to draw a picture of each type of marine mammal on the corresponding page.

Background Information

- There are four types of sea mammals: pinnipeds, cetaceans, sirenians, and sea otters.
- *Pinniped* comes from the Latin words meaning "fin-footed."
- Three types of pinnipeds are eared seals, earless seals, and walruses.
- *Cetaceans* are broken into two groups: baleen whales and toothed whales.
- Baleen whales do not have teeth.
- Toothed whales use *echolocation* to find their food.
- Manatees (sea cows) and dugongs are *sirenians*.
- Unlike many ocean animals, sea otters do not have a layer of blubber. Instead, they have thick fur that holds in air and keeps them from getting wet or cold.

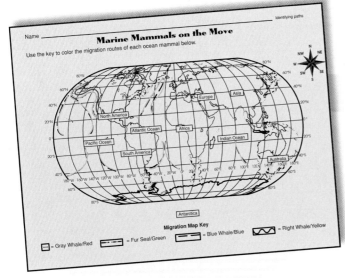

Marine Migration

Materials for each student:
copy of page 21

Review with students why ocean mammals migrate (to find warmer waters, locate food, or give birth to babies). Explain that many ocean mammals follow the same migration path each year. Then direct each child to use the map key to color the migration routes of gray whales, fur seals, blue whales, and right whales.

See the marine mammals skill sheet on page 22.

Life Science

Name _____ Identifying characteristics of mammals

Must Be a Mammal!

		Does it have hair or fur?	Does it have a backbone?	Does it have two pairs of limbs?	Does it drink milk from its mother?
horse					
grizzly bear					
earthworm					
elephant					
rabbit					
spider					
kangaroo					
chicken					
grasshopper					
human					

Bonus: On the back of this paper, list the animals that are not mammals. Then choose one and write a sentence telling how you know it is not a mammal.

20-Minute Science • ©The Mailbox® Books • TEC61364 • Key p.124

10 **Note to the teacher:** Use with "Must Be a Mammal!" on page 4.

MAMMAL INFO CIRCLE

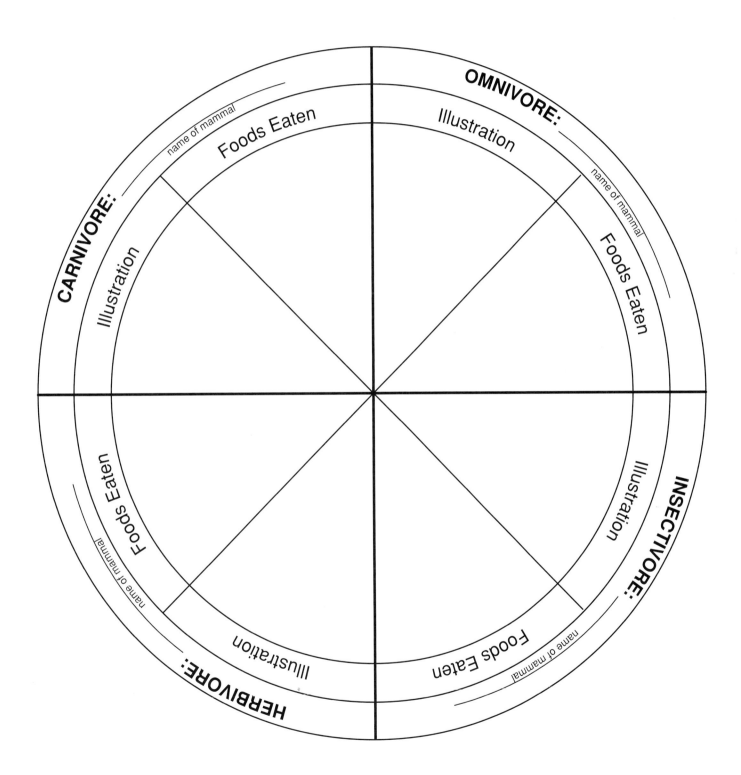

Note to the teacher: Use with "Hungry Mammals" on page 5.

Baby Animal Riddle Patterns

Use with "What Am I?" on page 5.

◇◇◇◇◇◇◇◇◇◇ **Baby Animal Riddle** ◇◇◇◇◇◇◇◇◇◇

I live in the _____.
　　　　　　　　　　　　　habitat, or where it lives

I look like _____.

I eat _____.

When I am a baby, I am called a _____

_____.

TEC61364

◇◇◇◇◇◇◇◇◇◇ **Baby Animal Riddle** ◇◇◇◇◇◇◇◇◇◇

I live in the _____.
　　　　　　　　　　　　　habitat, or where it lives

I look like _____.

I eat _____.

When I am a baby, I am called a _____

_____.

TEC61364

20-Minute Science • ©The Mailbox® Books • TEC61364

Home, Sweet Home

Make a ✓ in each box that shows that mammal's home(s).

	Wooded Area	Den	Nest	Burrow	Tunnel	Hollow Tree	Lodge
Bear							
Porcupine							
Skunk							
Fox							
Squirrel							
Chipmunk							
Rabbit							
Marmot							
Woodchuck							
Mole							
Mouse							
Deer							
Beaver							
Opossum							
Raccoon							
Marten							
Otter							
Muskrat							

Note to the teacher: Use with "Home, Sweet Home" on page 6.

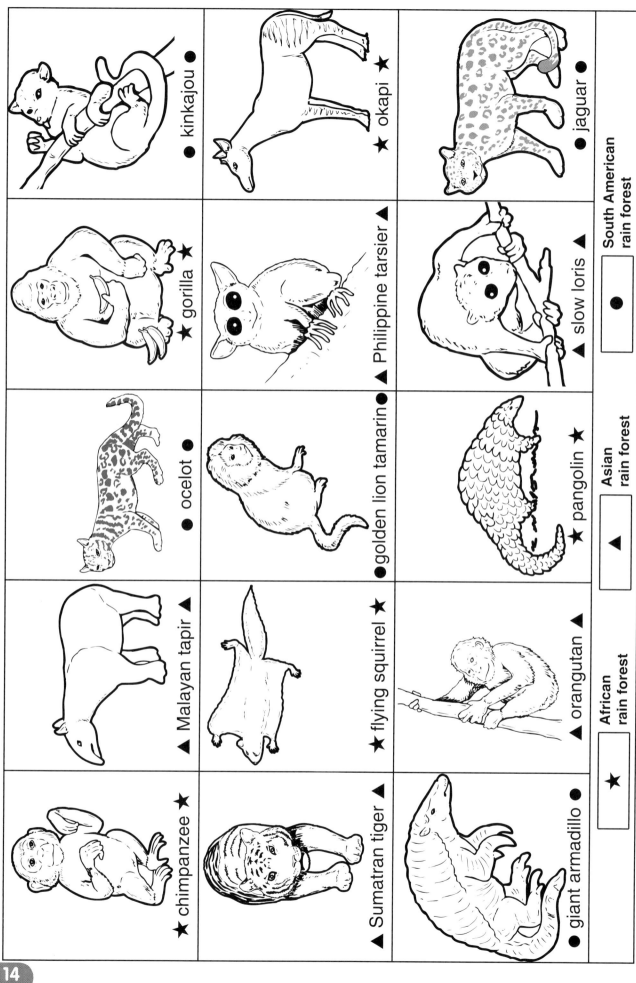

● kinkajou

★ okapi

● jaguar

★ gorilla

▲ Philippine tarsier

▲ slow loris

● ocelot

● golden lion tamarin

★ pangolin

▲ Malayan tapir

★ flying squirrel

▲ orangutan

★ chimpanzee

▲ Sumatran tiger

● giant armadillo

South American rain forest ●

Asian rain forest ▲

African rain forest ★

14

20-Minute Science • ©The Mailbox® Books • TEC61364

Note to the teacher: Use with "Which Rain Forest?" on page 6.

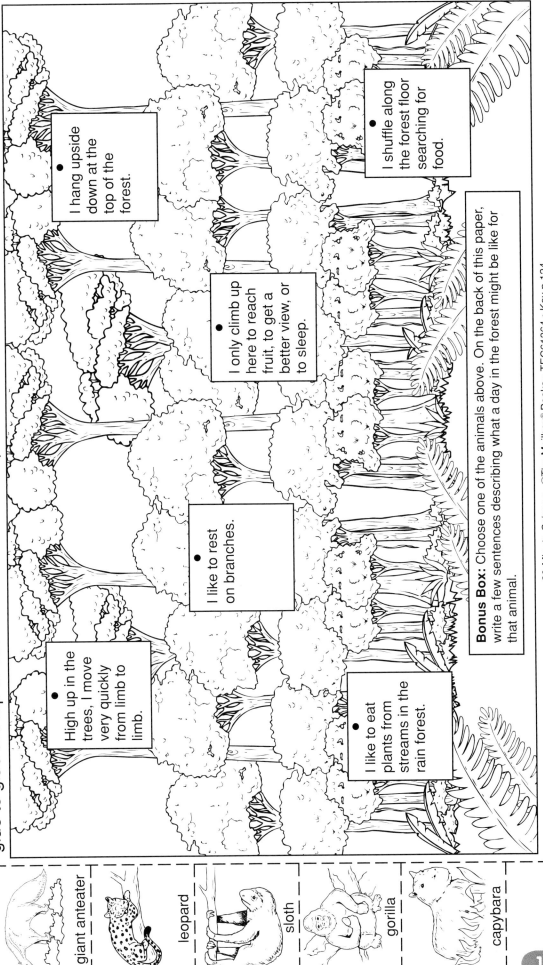

Name _____

Forest Dwelling

Many different mammals *dwell*, or live, in the rain forest. Some live high up in the trees, while others stay on the forest floor. Cut out the mammal cards. Read the information in each box; then use a dot of glue to glue the top of each card in the correct spot.

- I hang upside down at the top of the forest.

- I shuffle along the forest floor searching for food.

- I only climb up here to reach fruit, to get a better view, or to sleep.

- I like to rest on branches.

- High up in the trees, I move very quickly from limb to limb.

- I like to eat plants from streams in the rain forest.

Bonus Box: Choose one of the animals above. On the back of this paper, write a few sentences describing what a day in the forest might be like for that animal.

20-Minute Science • ©The Mailbox® Books • TEC61364 • Key p.124

spider monkey

giant anteater

leopard

sloth

gorilla

capybara

15

Animal Cards

Use with "Grassland Field Guide" on page 7.

TEC61364

TEC61364

TEC61364

TEC61364

TEC61364

TEC61364

TEC61364

TEC61364

20-Minute Science • ©The Mailbox® Books • TEC61364

Bison
(Prairie)

I am also called the American buffalo. I'm the largest American animal. I have a large hump on my back and hair that forms a beard under my chin. I'm brownish black on most of my body except for my hind part, which is just brown.

TEC61364

Prairie Dog
(Prairie)

I like to dig tunnels underground. These tunnels are where my family and I live. The tunnels also help the prairie grasses grow better. My furry coat is light brown.

TEC61364

Zebra
(Savanna)

I live in herds. I can run at speeds of up to 40 mph. I have an unusual coat with black-and-white stripes.

TEC61364

Warthog
(Savanna)

I like to eat plants, roots, birds' eggs, and small animals. I have two curved tusks. My body is gray, and it's thinly covered with very coarse brownish-gray hairs.

TEC61364

Giant Anteater
(Pampas)

I have very powerful claws that I use to break termite mud castles for food. I have a black band of hair bordered by white bands of hair that begin at my throat and run up to the middle of my back.

TEC61364

Maned Wolf
(Pampas)

I have really long legs that help me see over the tall grass when I'm searching for food (rodents, birds, insects). I have long yellowish-orange fur. It grows like a mane down the middle of my back.

TEC61364

Wild Horse
(Steppe)

I was the earth's last undomesticated horse. I disappeared from the steppes around 1947, but I was bred in captivity and recently put back in my natural home. I have a dark brown mane, a tan coat, and a white underbelly.

TEC61364

Saiga
(Steppe)

I'm Europe's only antelope. I have an unusual bulbous nose that helps warm and moisten cold, dry air. I have brown legs, and my body and head are light brown.

TEC61364

Name _____

Mammals Underground

_____
name of burrowing prairie mammal

Size: _____

Color: _____

What does it eat? _____

Where does it live? _____

Does it live in a family group? _____

What are its predators? _____

Draw an illustration of the mammal in its underground home.

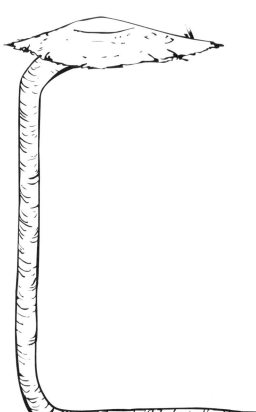

Note to the teacher: Use with "Prairie Basement" on page 7.

Name _____

Staying Cool

20-Minute Science • ©The Mailbox® Books • TEC61364 • Key p.124

Cape Ground Squirrel

Desert Bat

Collared Peccary

Fennec Fox

Jackrabbit

Coyote

Note to the teacher: Use with "Beat the Heat" on page 8.

Title Card and Fact Cards
Use with "Ocean Mammals" on page 9.

Ride the Waves With Ocean Mammals

20-Minute Science • ©The Mailbox® Books • TEC61364

Cetaceans

The two types of cetaceans are

_____ and _____ .

Baleen whales do not have _____ .

Toothed whales use _____

to find their food.

Pinnipeds

Three types of pinnipeds are

_____, _____, and

_____ .

The name *pinniped* comes from Latin words

meaning _____ .

Sirenians

The two types of sirenians are

_____ and _____ .

Manatees are sometimes called

_____ .

Sea Otters

Sea otters do not have a layer of

_____ .

Sea otters stay warm because of their

_____ .

Name _____

Marine Mammals on the Move

Use the key to color the migration routes of each ocean mammal below.

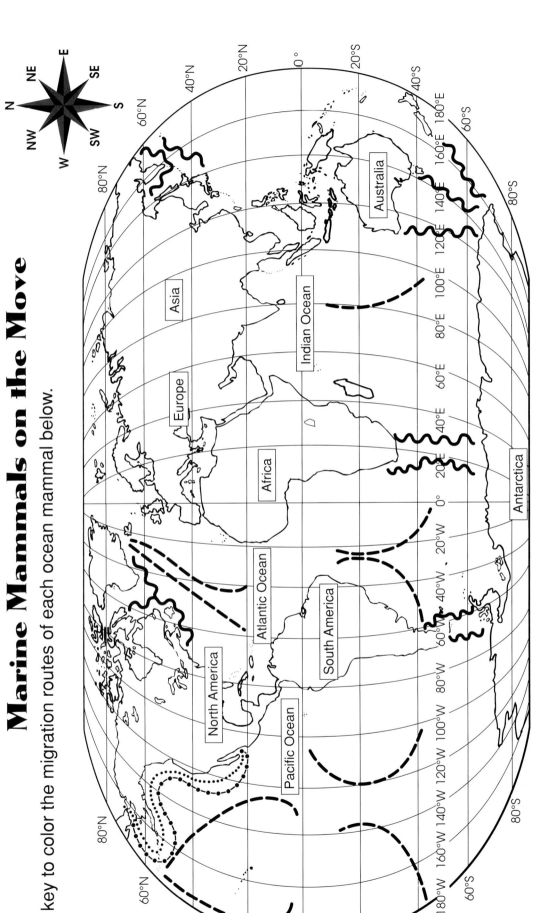

Migration Map Key

| : : : : : | = Gray Whale/Red | — · — · — | = Fur Seal/Green | — — — | = Blue Whale/Blue |

| ⟋⟍⟋⟍ | = Right Whale/Yellow |

20-Minute Science · ©The Mailbox® Books · TEC61364 · Key p.125

Note to the teacher: Use with "Marine Migration" on page 9.

Comparing Marine Mammals

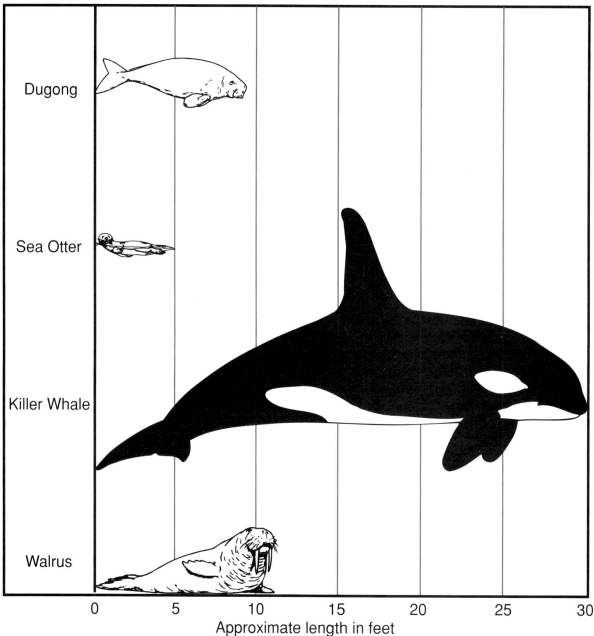

Approximate length in feet

Use the graph to answer the questions.

1. Which animal is 12 feet long? _____

2. Which animal is shorter than a walrus and longer than a sea otter? _____

3. Which animal is 30 feet long? _____

4. How many feet longer is the killer whale than the dugong? _____

5. List the animals from shortest to longest. _____

Amphibians and Reptiles

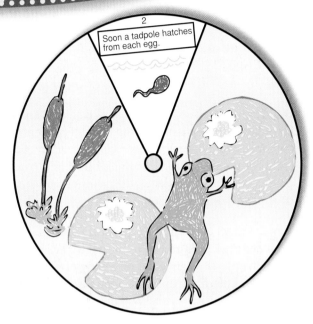

From Egg to Frog

Guide students through the steps below to help each child create a life cycle wheel of a frog.

Materials for each student:
copy of page 26
7" light blue construction paper circle with one triangular
    section cut out
brad

Steps:
1. Cut out the wheel pattern and information cards.
2. Read the cards and glue them in order on the wheel pattern.
3. Below each card, draw a picture to match the words.
4. Draw a frog habitat on the blue circle.
5. Place the blue circle atop the wheel and insert a brad through the center.
6. Turn the wheel to read about the life cycle of a frog.

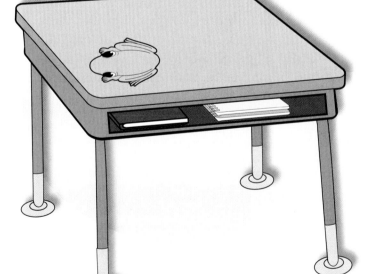

Hiding Out

Materials for each student:
copy of a frog pattern from page 27
tape

Explain to youngsters that frogs and toads can sometimes be eaten by animals such as snakes, birds, and even other frogs. The colors of some frogs and toads help camouflage them from these predators. Instruct each child to select an area in the classroom—such as a desk, on the carpet, or on the wall—where she can hide her frog. Then have each student color her frog to match her selected area. Have her tape her frog to that area. After each frog is in place, challenge individuals to find as many of the camouflaged frogs as they can.

Life Science

Salamanders and Newts

Materials for each student:
copy of pages 28, 29, and 30
access to reference materials

Day 1: Give each student a copy of pages 28 and 29. Have her write her name on the booklet cover and then follow the directions on each page. After each child has colored her illustrations, direct her to cut out the booklet pages, stack the pages behind the cover, and staple them along the left side.

Day 2: Direct each child to choose a salamander from her booklet to research. Then have her write the name of her salamander on a copy of page 30 and record her findings in the appropriate sections of the page.

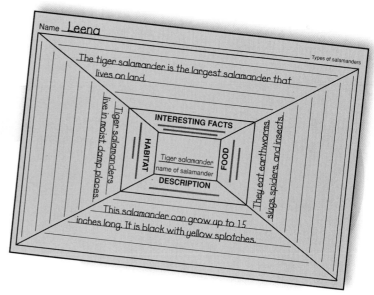

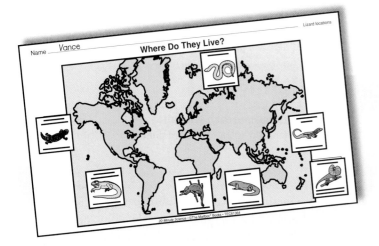

Lizards Around the World

Materials for each student:
copy of page 31

Explain to students that lizards live in many places around the world. Then have each child cut out the cards on his copy of page 31. Read aloud a lizard's name and the area in which it lives. Have each child find the matching card and guide him to glue it in the appropriate box on the map. Continue for each remaining card.

Did You Know?
Lizards are found on every continent except Antarctica.

Life Science

A Protective Shell

Materials:
2 raw eggs
palm-size rock
see-through unbreakable plastic storage container
small metal bowl
2 paper plates

Simulate the protective nature of a turtle's shell with this demonstration. In the see-through container, place an egg atop a paper plate. Ask students to predict what will happen to the egg if you drop the rock on it. Then drop the rock onto the egg from a few inches above and allow students to observe the results. Remove the damaged egg, plate, and rock. Then place another egg and plate in the container, inverting the metal bowl to cover the egg. Have students predict what will happen when you drop the rock this time. Drop the rock on the metal bowl; then lift the bowl to examine the egg. To conclude, explain that a turtle's body is fragile like the egg, but its shell—like the metal bowl—protects it from harm.

Did You Know?
Turtles are the only reptiles that have shells.

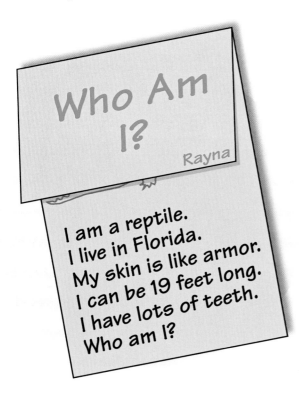

Who Am I?

Rayna

I am a reptile.
I live in Florida.
My skin is like armor.
I can be 19 feet long.
I have lots of teeth.
Who am I?

Who Am I?

Materials for each student:
12" x 18" construction paper
access to reference materials

Day 1: Have each child fold her construction paper into thirds. Then have her open the paper and, on the bottom third, write three or more clues about a reptile or amphibian of her choosing. (Invite her to use the reference materials if necessary.) Direct each child to draw in the middle section a picture of her chosen animal. Next, have her fold down the top third of her paper and add the title "Who Am I?"

Day 2: Invite each child, in turn, to share her clues with her classmates and reveal the picture when the animal is guessed correctly.

Life Science

Wheel Pattern and Information Cards

Use with "From Egg to Frog" on page 23.

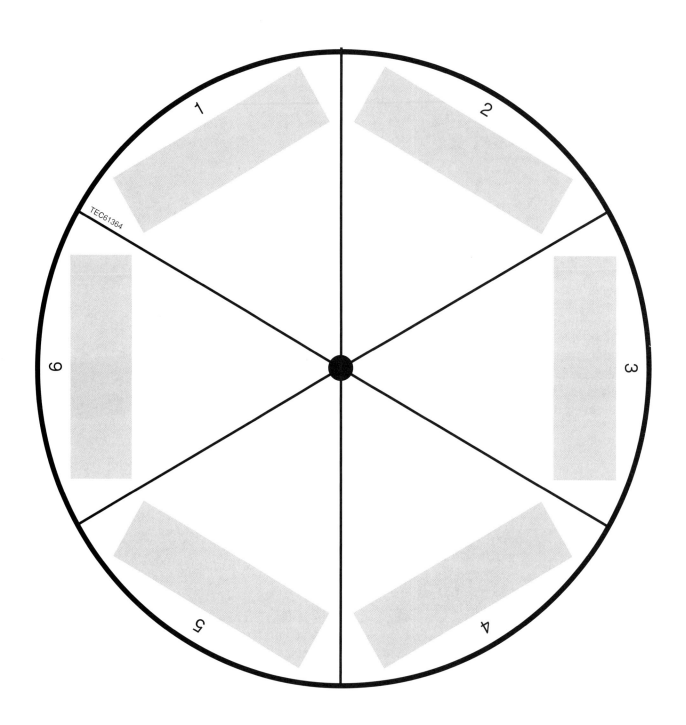

A female frog lays eggs in the pond.	Soon a tadpole hatches from each egg.	First, the tadpole's back legs begin to sprout.
Next, the front legs start to appear.	Then the tail starts to disappear.	Now a frog is ready to come out of the water.

TEC61364

TEC61364

Booklet Cover and Pages 1 and 2

Use with "Salamanders and Newts" on page 24.

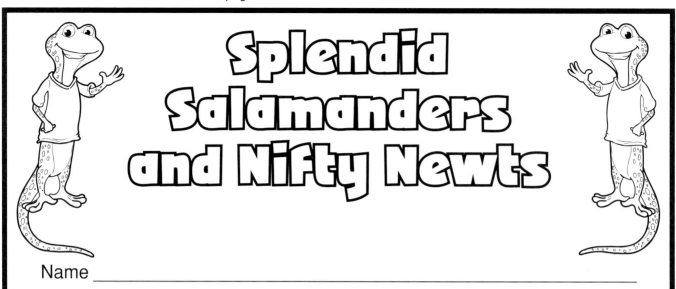

Splendid Salamanders and Nifty Newts

Name _____

20-Minute Science • ©The Mailbox® Books • TEC61364

Spotted Salamander

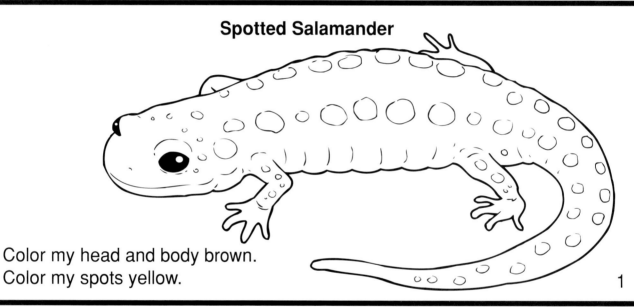

Color my head and body brown.
Color my spots yellow.

1

Marbled Salamander

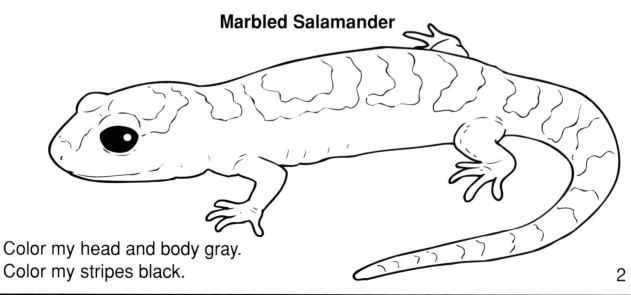

Color my head and body gray.
Color my stripes black.

2

Fire Salamander

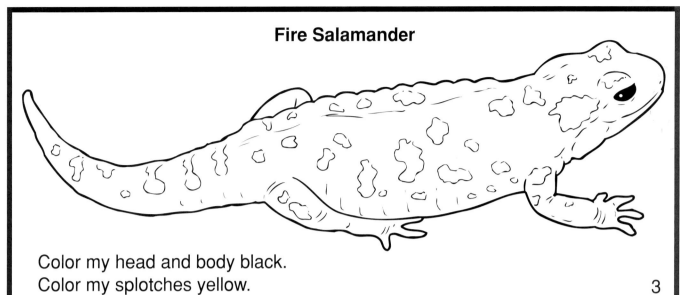

Color my head and body black.
Color my splotches yellow.

3

California Newt

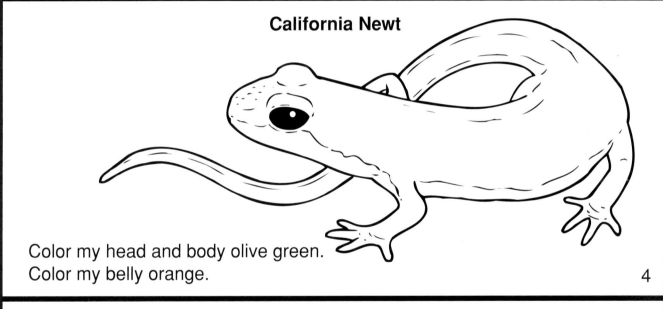

Color my head and body olive green.
Color my belly orange.

4

Tiger Salamander

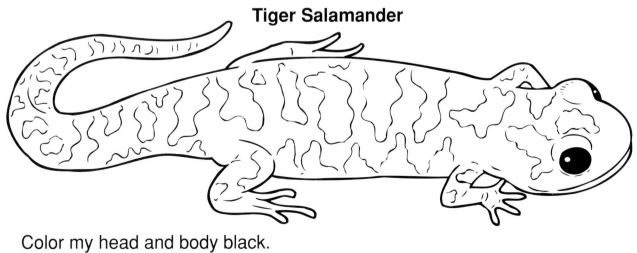

Color my head and body black.
Color my splotches yellow.

5

Types of salamanders

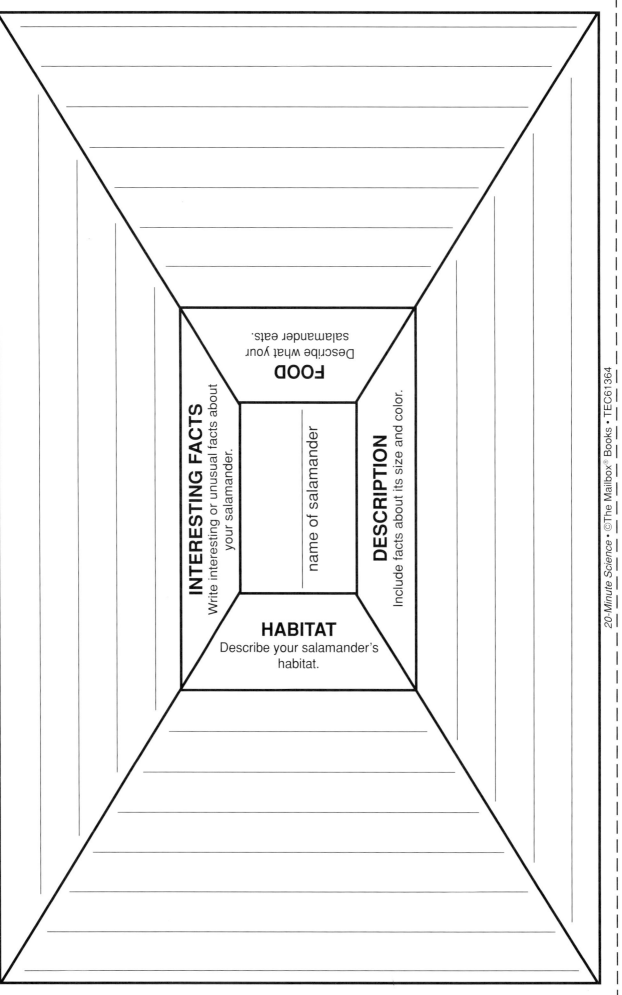

INTERESTING FACTS
Write interesting or unusual facts about your salamander.

FOOD
Describe what your salamander eats.

name of salamander

DESCRIPTION
Include facts about its size and color.

HABITAT
Describe your salamander's habitat.

20-Minute Science • ©The Mailbox® Books • TEC61364

Note to the teacher: Use with "Salamanders and Newts" on page 24.

Lizard locations

Where Do They Live?

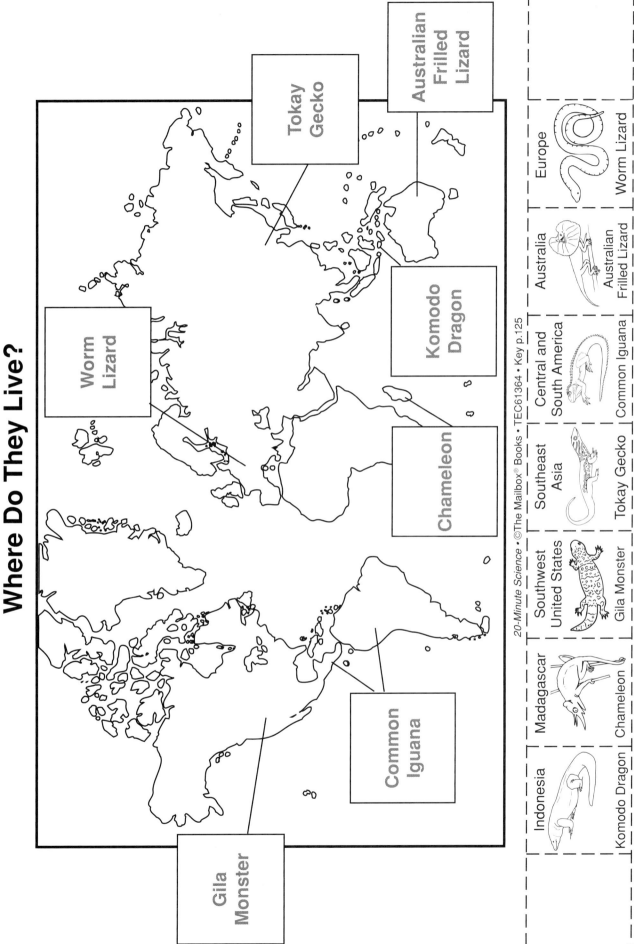

Gila Monster	Worm Lizard	Tokay Gecko	Australian Frilled Lizard	Komodo Dragon	Chameleon	Common Iguana

20-Minute Science • ©The Mailbox® Books • TEC61364 • Key p.125

Indonesia	Madagascar	Southwest United States	Southeast Asia	Central and South America	Australia	Europe
Komodo Dragon	Chameleon	Gila Monster	Tokay Gecko	Common Iguana	Australian Frilled Lizard	Worm Lizard

Note to the teacher: Use with "Lizards Around the World" on page 24.

Insects

Is It an Insect?

Materials:
copy of page 37, cut apart
chart similar to the one shown
paper bag

Put the cards in the bag. Then review with students the characteristics of an insect. Have each child pick a card from the bag and determine whether it shows an insect. Invite each child, in turn, to post his card in the appropriate column of the chart as he explains the reasons for his choice.

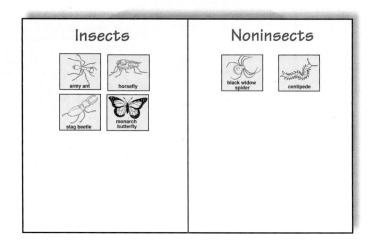

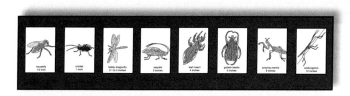

Insects by the Inch

Materials for each student:
copy of page 38
6" x 18" strip of construction paper

Remind students that insects come in all shapes and sizes. Tell them that some insects are less than an inch long while some are over a foot in length! Then have each child color and cut out a copy of the insect cards. Direct each child to glue her cards from smallest to largest on a strip of construction paper.

Life Science

Butterfly Life Cycle

Have youngsters make this model to review the developmental changes of butterflies.

Materials for each student:
9" paper plate
uncooked piece of the following pasta types: orzo, rotini, shell, and bow tie

Steps for students:
1. Divide the plate into four equal sections.
2. Label the sections as shown.
3. Glue each item to the appropriate section.
4. Add details to each section.

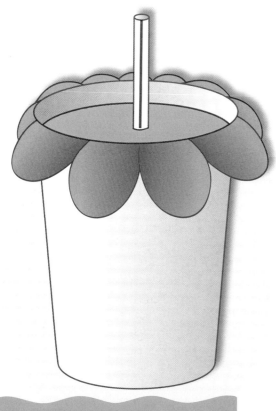

Super Sippers

Materials for each student:
construction paper scraps
juice or water
small paper cup
small straw
tape

Steps:
1. Explain to students that most butterflies suck nectar from flowers through a strawlike feeding tube called a *proboscis.*
2. Have each child use the construction paper scraps to make flower petals and tape them around the rim of his cup.
3. Pour a small amount of liquid (nectar) in each child's cup.
4. Have each student sip the nectar through his straw (proboscis).

Did You Know?
A butterfly's proboscis is usually coiled, but uncoils when the insect eats.

Life Science

Ladybug Model

To begin, explain to students that ladybugs have two sets of wings: an outer set, which gives the ladybug a hard covering that protects its body, and an inner set, which the ladybug uses to fly. Then lead students in making the model to illustrate the ladybug's unusual wings.

Materials for each student:
copy of page 39
9" x 12" sheet of red construction paper
sheet of white tissue paper

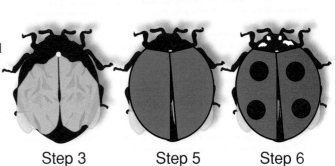

Step 3   Step 5   Step 6

Steps for students:

1. Color the body and spot patterns; then cut them out.
2. Trace the inner wings on the tissue paper and cut them out. Gently wrinkle them.
3. Glue the pointed end of each tissue paper wing to the body as shown.
4. Trace the two outer wings on the red paper; then cut them out.
5. Glue the top edge of each outer wing to the body as shown.
6. Glue two spots onto each outer wing.

Did You Know?
Ladybugs belong to a group of animals called *coleoptera*, which means "sheath wing."

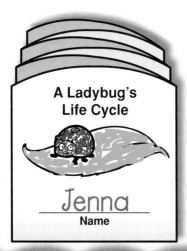

A Ladybug's Life Cycle

Jenna
Name

Ladybug Life Cycle

Materials for each student:
copy of page 40

Steps for students:

1. Color and cut out the booklet sections. Personalize the cover.
2. Glue page 2 to page 3 where indicated.
3. Cut out the cards and glue each card in the box below its corresponding picture.
4. Accordion-fold the booklet pages so the cover is on top.

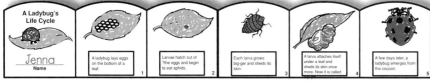

A Ladybug's Life Cycle — Jenna — Name

A ladybug lays eggs on the bottom of a leaf. 1

Larvae hatch out of ?the eggs and begin to eat aphids. 2

Each larva grows big-ger and sheds its skin. 3

A larva attaches itself under a leaf and sheds its skin once more. Now it is called 4

A few days later, a ladybug emerges from the cocoon. 5

Life Science

Honeybee Anatomy

Materials for each student:
copy of page 41

Name each bee part listed in the color code. Then read aloud each clue, in turn, and guide each child to label on his page the part that matches each description. When all the parts are labeled, have each child color each box by the code.

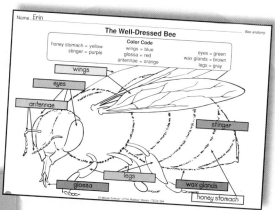

Clues:

1. All six of us are connected at the thorax. Two of us carry pollen in special pockets and two of us help clean pollen from the body. *(legs)*
2. In the abdomen, we produce the wax that the bee uses to make the honeycomb. *(wax glands)*
3. The bee uses me like a straw to suck water, nectar, and honey into its mouth. *(glossa)*
4. A bee doesn't have a nose, so we do all the smelling. *(antennae)*
5. As the bee collects nectar from each flower it visits, I store the nectar. *(honey stomach)*
6. We work together to help the bee move up, down, backward, and forward or to hover like a helicopter. *(wings)*
7. The bee dies after it uses me to inject poison into its enemy. *(stinger)*
8. The bee has five of us altogether. Three of us are in a triangle on top of the head. The other two, found on each side of the head, are much larger and have thousands of lenses to help the bee find food and spot enemies. *(eyes)*

The Pollination Process

Materials:
container, decorated as shown
baby powder
class supply of yellow pom-poms

Place the pom-poms (nectar) in the container and then place a layer of baby powder (pollen) atop the pom-poms. Have each student take one pom-pom. Point out several students who have baby powder on their hands. Discuss how this is similar to how bees collect pollen from flowers. When a bee lands on a flower, it becomes dusted with pollen. Then, when the bee lands on a different flower, some of the pollen falls off the bee and pollinates that flower.

Life Science

Crickets & Grasshoppers

Follow up a study of crickets and grasshoppers with this comparison activity!

Materials for each student:
copy of page 42
9" x 12" sheet of construction paper

Steps for students:
1. Fold the construction paper into three equal sections. Unfold the paper.
2. Color and cut out the heading cards at the top of page 42. Glue each card at the top of a different section of the paper.
3. Read the fact cards in rows A and B. Then label each card "cricket," "grasshopper," or "both."
4. Write an appropriate fact on each card in row C.
5. Cut out the cards and glue each card in the correct column.

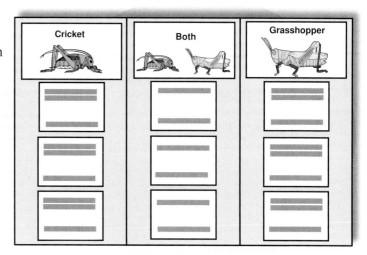

Did You Know?
Both crickets and grasshoppers lay eggs, but crickets lay one egg at a time while grasshoppers lay 20–120 eggs at a time. Both crickets and grasshoppers shed their exoskeletons, or *molt*, as they grow.

A Grasshopper's Life Cycle

Materials for each student:
construction paper copy of page 43
brad fastener

Steps for students:
1. Color and cut out the patterns. Cut out the viewing window on the aquarium where indicated.
2. Push the brad through the dot in the center of the aquarium cutout.
3. Place the wheel underneath the aquarium and push the brad through the dot in the center of the wheel. Bend the ends of the brad to secure.
4. Turn the wheel clockwise to view the stages of a grasshopper's life.

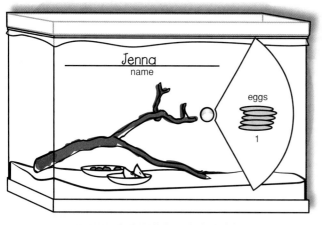

Life Science

stag beetle	snakefly	army ant	water boatman	tarantula
TEC61364	TEC61364	TEC61364	TEC61364	TEC61364
walkingstick	mosquito	monarch butterfly	fruit fly	giant water bug
TEC61364	TEC61364	TEC61364	TEC61364	TEC61364
leaf insect	fire ant	scorpion	cotton boll moth	head louse
TEC61364	TEC61364	TEC61364	TEC61364	TEC61364
crab spider	crane fly	rove beetle	biddy dragonfly	aphid
TEC61364	TEC61364	TEC61364	TEC61364	TEC61364
goliath beetle	centipede	swallowtail butterfly	stinkbug	cat flea
TEC61364	TEC61364	TEC61364	TEC61364	TEC61364
tick	harvestman	horsefly	black widow spider	praying mantis
TEC61364	TEC61364	TEC61364	TEC61364	TEC61364

20-Minute Science • ©The Mailbox® Books • TEC61364 • Key p.125

Note to the teacher: Use with "Is It an Insect?" on page 32.

37

Insect Cards

Use with "Insects by the Inch" on page 32.

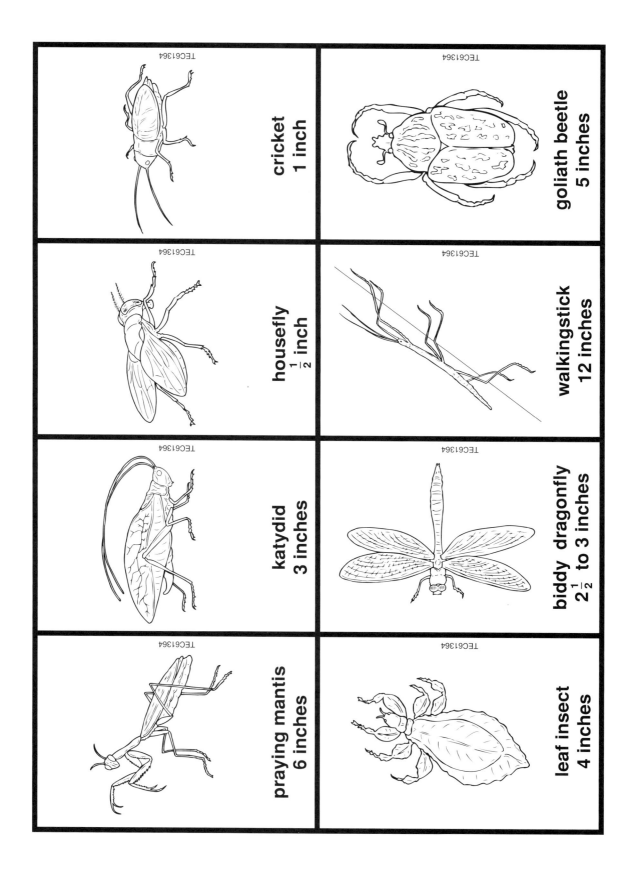

cricket
1 inch
TEC61364

goliath beetle
5 inches
TEC61364

housefly
$\frac{1}{2}$ inch
TEC61364

walkingstick
12 inches
TEC61364

katydid
3 inches
TEC61364

biddy dragonfly
$2\frac{1}{2}$ to 3 inches
TEC61364

praying mantis
6 inches
TEC61364

leaf insect
4 inches
TEC61364

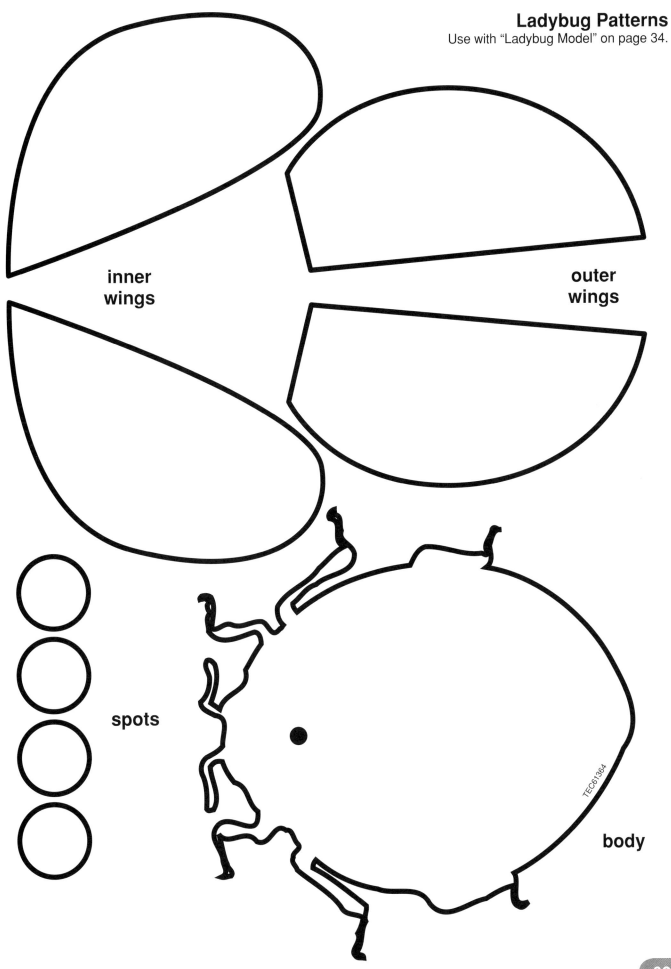

inner
wings

outer
wings

spots

body

Life Cycle Booklet and Cards

Use with "Ladybug Life Cycle" on page 34.

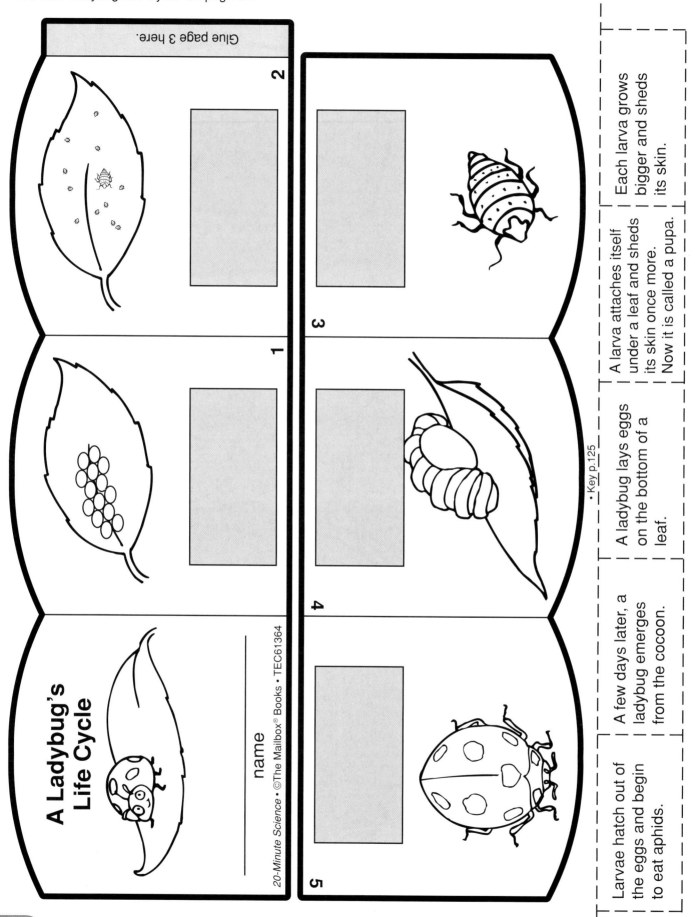

Glue page 3 here.

2

1

A Ladybug's
Life Cycle

name

20-Minute Science • ©The Mailbox® Books • TEC61364

3

4

5

• Key p.125

Each larva grows
bigger and sheds
its skin.

A larva attaches itself
under a leaf and sheds
its skin once more.
Now it is called a pupa.

A ladybug lays eggs
on the bottom of a
leaf.

A few days later, a
ladybug emerges
from the cocoon.

Larvae hatch out of
the eggs and begin
to eat aphids.

Name _____

The Well-Dressed Bee

Color Code

honey stomach = yellow
stinger = purple

wings = blue
glossa = red
antennae = orange

eyes = green
wax glands = brown
legs = gray

20-Minute Science • ©The Mailbox® Books • TEC61364 • Key p.126

Note to the teacher: Use with "Honeybee Anatomy" on page 35.

41

Heading Cards and Fact Cards
Use with "Crickets & Grasshoppers" on page 36.

Grasshopper

TEC61364

Both

TEC61364

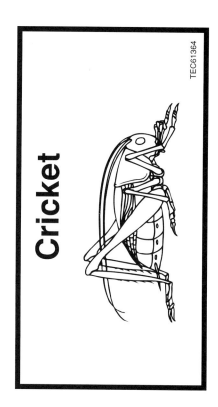

Cricket

TEC61364

A

B

C

A	B	C
I sing by rubbing my wings together.	I prefer to eat plants.	_____ _____ . **both**
My babies are called nymphs.	I eat plants and other insects.	_____ _____ . **grasshopper**
I can't fly.	I can fly.	_____ _____ . **cricket**

20-Minute Science • ©The Mailbox® Books • TEC61364 • Key p.126

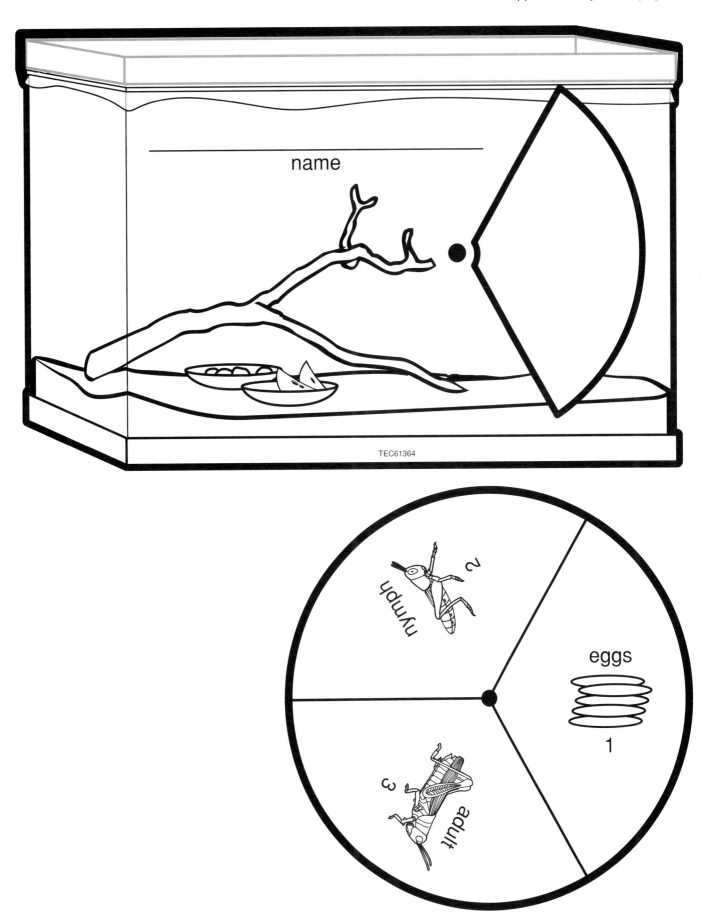

name

TEC61364

eggs

1

nymph

2

adult

3

Plant Parts

Plant Parts

Materials for each student:
copy of page 53
9" x 12" sheet of construction paper

Review the different parts of a plant with students. Then have each child cut apart his copy of page 53. Direct him to assemble the puzzle pieces to make a plant and glue the pieces in place on the construction paper. Next, have him match each definition with its plant part label and glue the definition and label by the corresponding puzzle piece.

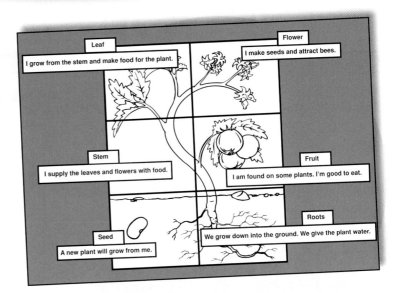

Leaf
I grow from the stem and make food for the plant.

Flower
I make seeds and attract bees.

Stem
I supply the leaves and flowers with food.

Fruit
I am found on some plants. I'm good to eat.

Seed
A new plant will grow from me.

Roots
We grow down into the ground. We give the plant water.

Edible Plant Parts

Roots
radish
carrot
beet

Seeds
peas
beans
nuts

Fruits
apple
pear
peach

Stems
celery
asparagus

Flowers
broccoli
cauliflower

Leaves
lettuce
spinach
cabbage

Eat Up!

Materials for each student:
copy of page 54

Day 1: Explain to students that they eat many different plant parts—roots, stems, leaves, seeds, fruits, and flowers—every day. List each plant part on the board. Then name a food that is a plant part. Help students determine which plant part the food is as you write it under the appropriate heading. Continue naming foods until several examples of each plant part are listed.

Day 2: Review with students the foods that are plant parts and which parts they are. Then have each child complete a copy of page 54.

Life Science

Parts of a Seed

Materials:
class supply of copies of page 55
class supply of dried lima beans soaked in red-tinted
    water overnight (The red food coloring makes it
    easier to distinguish the seed parts.)
paper towels
class supply of toothpicks

Tell youngsters that seeds have three parts: the embryo, the seed coat, and the cotyledon. Then give each child a presoaked bean on a paper towel and a toothpick. Have each child use her toothpick to carefully remove the seed coat from her bean and glue it to the box on page 55 labeled "Seed Coat." Then guide her to gently separate the two cotyledons. Explain that the cotyledon with the leafy structure is the embryo with food tissue and the other cotyledon is just food tissue. Direct each child to glue each cotyledon in the appropriate box. Then have her label each seed part on the diagram.

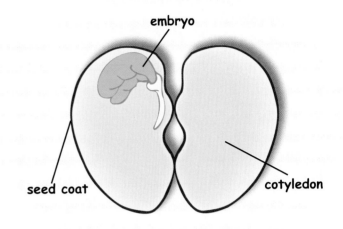

embryo

seed coat

cotyledon

Did You Know?
The *embryo* contains the new plant parts beginning to grow inside the seed.
The *seed coat* protects the new plant.
The *cotyledon* is the food storage tissue of the seed.

Seed Movers

wind
water
bird
girl
boy
dog

Seed Movers

Materials:
tree-shaped chart, titled as shown
class supply of cotton balls, plus four or five more

Remind students that when a plant or tree releases its seeds, they fall to the ground close to the parent plant unless something moves them. Then encourage students to brainstorm seed movers—such as animals, wind, and people—as you list their ideas on the chart. Next, place the cotton balls on the floor beneath the chart (parent plant) and ask students to pretend the cotton balls are seeds. Have each child, in turn, take a cotton ball (seed) and move it to a different location as he states what kind of a seed mover he is and how he is moving the seed. For example, he might say, "I am the wind. I blow my seed across the street." When each child has taken his turn, explain that the seeds left close to the parent plant represent seeds that remain where they fell.

Life Science

Seed Study

Materials for each student:
copy of page 56
seed packet (use a variety of seed types)
paper plate

Day 1: Instruct each child to pour the contents of her seed packet onto a paper plate. Then have each child complete her copy of page 56, using the information on the seed packet as needed.

Day 2: Direct each child to review the information on her page. Then have her place it on her desk beside her plate. Invite students to walk from desk to desk viewing the different seeds and information. Challenge students to find information such as the fastest and slowest germinating seeds or the plants that would be harvested first and last. After students have finished their observations, lead them in discussing their findings.

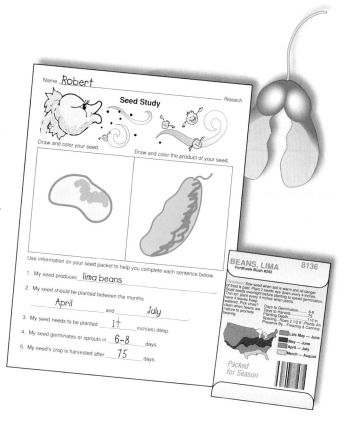

Seeds Down Under

Use this activity to let your students witness firsthand the changes that take place in a seed underground after it has been planted. After guiding students through the steps below, tack the finished projects to a bulletin board. Then encourage students to check their seeds daily.

Materials for each student:
2 resealable plastic bags, one labeled with the child's name
aquarium gravel
potting soil
3–4 seeds (lima bean or other large seed)

Steps for students:
1. Put one inch of aquarium gravel in the bottom of the bag labeled with your name.
2. Snip off the bottom corners of the second bag (for drainage) and fit it in the bag with the gravel (both zippered openings at the top).
3. Place about four inches of potting soil in the inner bag.
4. Plant the seeds about two inches deep, making sure one side of each seed is visible from the outside of the bags.
5. Water the top of the soil; then seal the bags.
6. Check your seeds daily and record your observations.

Life Science

Smart Plants

Remind students that a plant's roots grow downward to seek moisture while its stem grows upward toward the sunlight. Ask students what they think would happen if a plant were turned upside down. Then have students follow the steps below to test their predictions.

Materials for each student:
small resealable plastic bag
lima bean seed
2 paper towels
water

Steps for students:
1. Wet the paper towels and place them in the bag.
2. Put the seed between the bag and a paper towel so it can be seen.
3. Zip the bag closed and hang it according to your teacher's directions.

Observation: Check the bag daily to ensure that the towels are still damp. Add water if needed. When a root begins to grow from one end of the seed, and a stem grows from the other, turn your bag upside down and rehang it so the roots are pointing up and the stem down. Several days after the plants start to grow, guide students to realize that no matter how a plant is turned, its roots will grow down and its stem will grow up. Check the bags for several more days, making sure the towels stay damp.

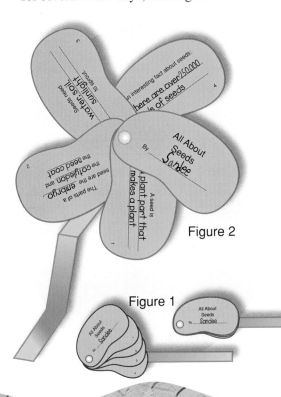

Figure 2

Figure 1

All About Seeds

After reviewing information about seeds, invite students to complete these booklets.

Materials for each student:
construction paper copy of page 57
1" x 12" green construction paper strip
brad
access to a hole puncher

Steps for students:
1. Complete each sentence and personalize the booklet cover; then cut out the booklet pages and cover.
2. Hole-punch the dot on each page and one end of the green strip.
3. Stack the pages in order and place the green strip at the bottom of the stack. Align all the holes.
4. Secure the pieces together with a brad. *(Fig. 1)*
5. Accordion-fold the green strip so it is hidden behind the pages.
6. Fan out the pages and unfold the stem. *(Fig. 2)*

Flower Parts

To begin, draw a simple sketch of a flower on the board. Review the parts of a flower and enlist students' help in labeling them. Then review the function of each part.

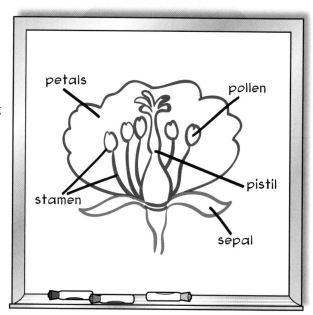

Flower Parts

petals: shelter the inside parts of the flower

sepals: make up the outermost part of the flower and help protect the inner parts of the flower

pistil: a tube-like structure that is the female part of a flower

stamens: the stalks that surround the pistil; the male part of a flower

pollen: dust held by each stamen

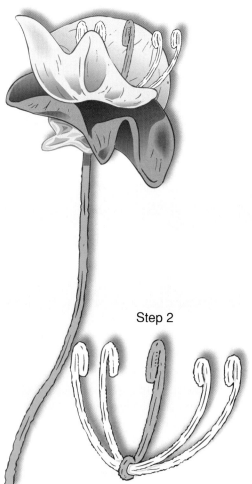

Step 2

3-D Models

Review each plant part's function with students as you guide them through the steps below.

Materials for each student:
green pipe cleaner
yellow pipe cleaner, cut in half
4" orange pipe cleaner length
3" green tissue paper circle
two 7" tissue paper circles

Steps for students:

1. Fold over the ends of each yellow pipe cleaner half. Hold the pieces together and bend them in half so they look like stamens.
2. Fold over one end of the orange pipe cleaner. Wrap the other end around the stamens, as shown, so that it looks like a pistil.
3. Wrap one end of the green pipe cleaner around the stamens so that it resembles a stem.
4. Carefully poke the stem through the center of one of the large tissue paper circles. Squeeze a thin line of glue around the center of the circle and pinch the resulting petal at the base of the stamens and pistil.
5. Repeat Step 4 with the second large tissue paper circle to make another petal and then with the small green circle to make a sepal.

Life Science

Life Cycle of a Flower

Before making these projects, review with students each stage in a flower's life cycle.

Materials for each student:
copy of the flower center patterns from page 58
4 colorful construction paper copies of a flower pattern
    from page 58
loose-leaf binder ring
access to a hole puncher

Steps for students:
1. Cut out the flower centers and flowers.
2. Hole-punch each flower where indicated.
3. Glue each flower center to a different flower, keeping the holes in the flowers at the top.
4. Stack the flowers in order and use the ring to fasten them together.
5. Read the project to review the life cycle of a flower.

A seed sprouts.
A stem and
roots grow.

Environments

desert: hot days, cold nights, very dry

grassland: thick grass, pastures, roadsides

mountain: cold nights, strong sunlight, windy

seashore: bright sunlight; strong wind; rocky, sandy, or muddy shores

tropics: dark and shady, humid, warm or hot

waterside: damp or wet, at the sides of lakes and streams

Wildflower Adaptations

Materials for each student:
copy of page 59

Remind students that flowers need light, water, air, and nutrients to survive. Discuss how people who care for plants meet those needs. Then point out that wildflowers do not usually receive any special care and are completely dependent on their natural environments. Review the characteristics of the environments shown on page 59. Invite students to share their ideas about traits a flower might need to survive in each of these environments. Then have each child complete his copy of the page.

Life Science

Tree Roots

After this demonstration, guide students to realize that roots help support trees and anchor them in the ground.

Materials:
green construction paper tree cutout
clear cup partially filled with sand
drinking straw
tape

Steps:

1. Stand the tree cutout in the cup without pushing it down. Have students predict what might happen to the tree if you let go. Then have them observe what happens. *(The tree falls over.)*

2. Push the tree about one-half inch into the sand. Invite students to predict what will happen to the tree when you let go. Have them observe what happens. *(The tree remains standing.)*

3. Ask students to predict how wind might affect the tree. Then blow on the tree to simulate a windy day. Have students observe what happens. *(The tree falls over.)*

4. Tape the tree to a straw about three inches from the bottom of the straw. Push the straw down until the base of the tree touches the sand. Invite students to predict what will happen to the tree when you blow on it. Blow on the tree and have them observe the results. *(The tree remains standing.)*

In the Trees

Materials for each student:
copy of page 60
12" x 18" sheet on construction paper

To begin, have each child draw on her construction paper a tree with roots, a trunk, branches, and leaves. Remind students that the animals on the cards rely on trees for food and shelter. Discuss with students which animals need food from trees, which need shelter, and which need both. Then have each child cut out the critter cards and glue them on, in, and under the tree depending on where she thinks the animals would normally be found.

Life Science

Leaves in Action

These experiments demonstrate to students a leaf's task of continually releasing oxygen and water from a plant.

Materials for each group:
healthy leaf
clear plastic bowl
several magnifying glasses
a healthy, leafy plant
plastic sandwich bag
length of string
water

Day 1: Release of oxygen

Have each child in a small group use a magnifying glass to examine the leaf. Ask students whether they can see anything coming off of the surface of the leaf. *(No.)* Next, have one group member place the leaf in the bowl. Direct another group member to pour in enough water to cover the leaf. Have the group observe its leaf and describe what's happening. *(Bubbles are forming and rising off the leaf.)* Explain to students that the bubbles they see are oxygen escaping from the plant through the *stomata* (tiny holes that cover the leaf).

Day 2: Release of water

Cover one leaf of the plant with a plastic bag and secure it with string. Then water the plant and place it in a sunny window. Throughout the day, invite students to observe changes that take place. *(Drops of water collect on the inside of the plastic bag.)* At the end of the day, invite students to share their observations. Explain that water is absorbed from the soil by the plant's roots. It then moves up the stem to the leaves. The process of *transpiration* occurs when the plant releases water through the stomata in the leaf.

Life Science

Plant Parts

The Life of a Leaf

Guide each child through the steps below to make a leaf life-cycle model. After each child completes his model, lead students in singing the song shown. Direct each child to use his model as he sings.

Materials for each student:
half of a paper towel tube
3" x 6" leaf cutouts in the following colors: 2 green, 1 brown,
   1 yellow, and 1 orange
green pipe cleaner
access to a hole puncher

Steps for students:
1. Stack the five leaves together, placing a green leaf on the top and bottom of the stack.
2. Punch a hole through the wide end of the leaves.
3. Loop one end of the pipe cleaner through the holes and twist it to secure it.
4. Insert the pipe cleaner into the top of the tube and pull until the leaves are hidden in the tube.

The Life of a Leaf
(sung to the tune of "The Itsy-Bitsy Spider")

A leaf begins its life as a bud so very small.
   (Poke the tip of the leaves out of the tube.)
It grows for several weeks, till it's full-grown, green, and tall.
   (Push the leaves all the way out of the tube.)
Spring and summer pass as it dances in the breeze.
   (Wave tube to move the leaves.)
Then, in fall, it changes color,
   (Spread out the five leaves.)
Lets go, and drops with ease.
   (Push the leaves out of the tube and let them drop to the floor.)

Enlightening Leaves

Materials:
class supply of copies of page 61
leafy green plant (such as an African violet)
piece of construction paper trimmed to fit over one of the plant's
   leaves, with a small circle cut in the center of it
paper clips

Use paper clips to attach the construction paper to the top of a leaf. Then set the plant in direct sunlight. Guide each student to record on his copy of page 61 how the experiment was prepared and his hypothesis (what he thinks will happen). Over the next five days, have students record their observations about the leaf. At the end of the five days, remove the paper from the leaf and have students examine the change in the leaf. Guide students to realize that the section of the leaf not covered by paper is a darker green than the covered sections. Explain that this is because the uncovered part received more sunlight and absorbed more energy than the covered parts.

Did You Know?
Chlorophyll absorbs energy from sunlight to make food for a plant. It gives leaves their green color.

Life Science

Name _____

Plant Puzzle

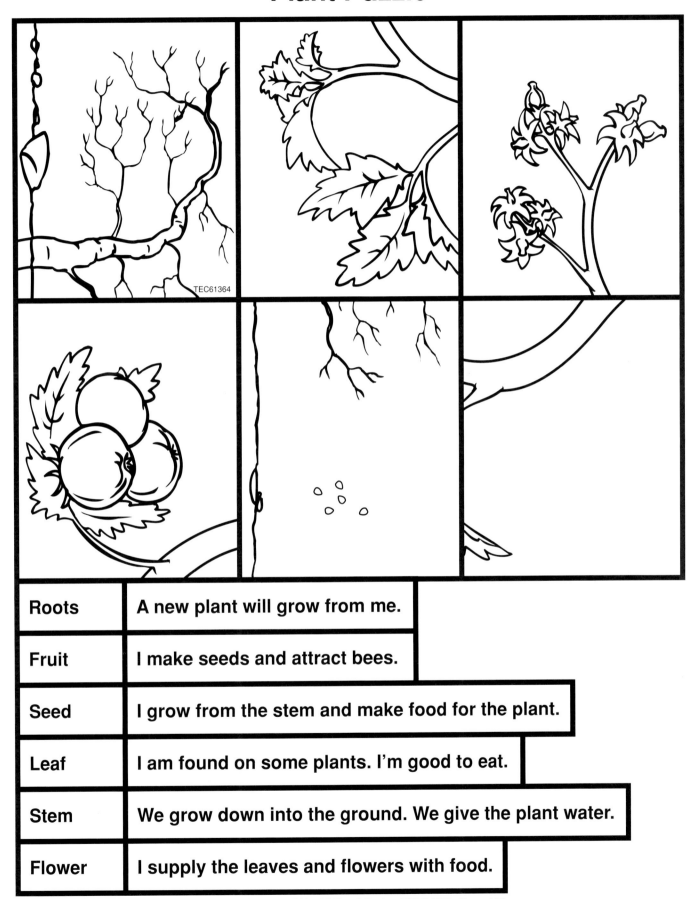

Roots	A new plant will grow from me.
Fruit	I make seeds and attract bees.
Seed	I grow from the stem and make food for the plant.
Leaf	I am found on some plants. I'm good to eat.
Stem	We grow down into the ground. We give the plant water.
Flower	I supply the leaves and flowers with food.

20-Minute Science • ©The Mailbox® Books • TEC61364 • Key p.127

Note to the teacher: Use with "Plant Parts" on page 44.

How Does Your Garden Grow?

Cut out the cards below. Glue them in place in the garden. Write the name of the
fruit or vegetable in the correct spot on the garden key.

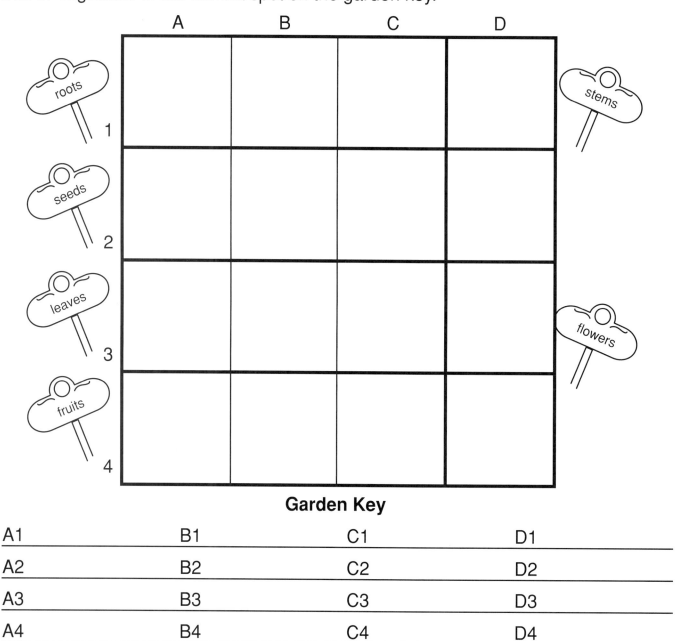

Garden Key

A1 _____	B1 _____	C1 _____	D1 _____
A2 _____	B2 _____	C2 _____	D2 _____
A3 _____	B3 _____	C3 _____	D3 _____
A4 _____	B4 _____	C4 _____	D4 _____

20-Minute Science • ©The Mailbox® Books • TEC61364 • Key p.127

Name_____

Parts of a Seed

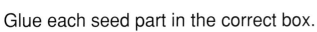

Glue each seed part in the correct box.

Seed Coat	Embryo	Cotyledon

Label the seed.

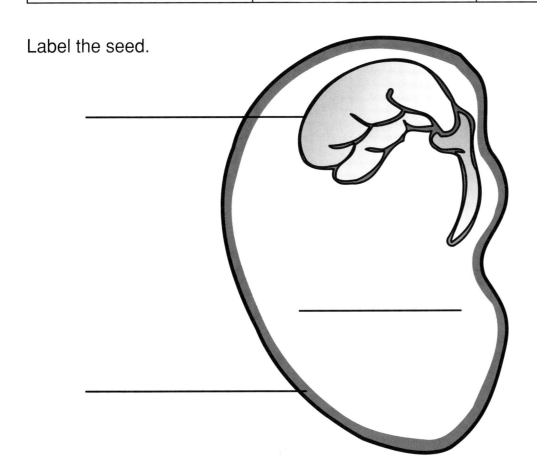

Note to the teacher: Use with "Parts of a Seed" on page 45.

Seed Study

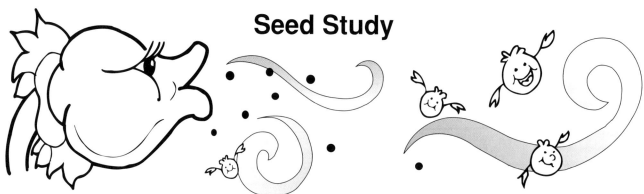

Draw and color your seed.   Draw and color the product of your seed.

Use information on your seed packet to help you complete each sentence below.

1. My seed produces _____.

2. My seed should be planted between the months _____

   and _____.

3. My seed needs to be planted _____ inch(es) deep.

4. My seed germinates or sprouts in _____ days.

5. My seed's crop is harvested after _____ days.

20-Minute Science • ©The Mailbox® Books • TEC61364

56 **Note to the teacher:** Use with "Seed Study" on page 46.

All About Seeds

By _____

20-Minute Science • ©The Mailbox® Books • TEC61364

Seeds need _____ to sprout.

3

A seed is _____

_____

_____.

1

An interesting fact about seeds:

_____

_____.

4

The parts of a seed are the

_____, the

_____, and

the _____.

2

Flower and Flower Center Patterns
Use with "Life Cycle of a Flower" on page 49.

Seeds fall from the plant.

A seed sprouts. A stem and roots grow.

The flowers die. Seeds grow.

The new plant grows leaves and flowers.

TEC61364

TEC61364

20-Minute Science • ©The Mailbox® Books • TEC61364

Name_____

True Survivors

Read the box to the right.
Read about each flower below.
Choose the best environment for each flower.
Complete the sentences.

1. 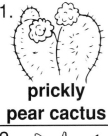 **prickly pear cactus**	Being thirsty is never a problem for me! I have lots of roots. They soak up water and store it for a long time. My home is a _____.
2. 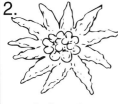 **edelweiss**	I have a thick, woolly coat of hairs that trap the warm sun. They also protect me from the wind. My home is a _____.
3.  **orchid**	I live where there are many trees. I climb on the trees so I can see the sun. My home is the _____.
4. 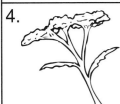 **yarrow**	I can grow in thick grass because I am tough. Sometimes I grow by the side of the road. My home is a _____.
5.  **sea holly**	My stems are strong. They help me grow on rocky shores. They protect me from wind too. My home is the _____.
6.  **water crowfoot**	My big leaves at the top get sunlight. My tiny leaves at the bottom let the stream move by easily. My home is the _____.

Environments

desert: hot days, cold nights, very dry

grassland: thick grass, pastures, roadsides

mountain: cold nights, strong sunlight, windy

seashore: bright sunlight; strong wind; rocky, sandy, or muddy shores

tropics: dark and shady, humid, warm or hot

waterside: damp or wet, at the sides of lakes and streams

Bonus: If you could live in any of the environments listed above, which would you choose? Why? Write your answer on the back of this sheet.

20-Minute Science • ©The Mailbox® Books • TEC61364 • Key p.127

Note to the teacher: Use with "Wildflower Adaptations" on page 49.

Critter Cards
Use with "In the Trees" on page 50.

butterfly

robin

mouse

bee

woodpecker

squirrel

caterpillar

titmouse

chipmunk

spider

chickadee

opossum

Leave It to Us

1. Experiment:
What I did…

_____

_____

_____

Draw Experiment

2. Hypothesis:
What I think will happen…

_____

_____

_____

Draw Observation

3. Observation:
What I saw…

_____

_____

_____

4. Conclusion:
What happened and why…

_____

_____

_____

Draw Conclusion

20-Minute Science • ©The Mailbox® Books • TEC61364

Note to the teacher: Use with "Enlightening Leaves" on page 52.

Light

Types of Light

Materials for each student:
construction paper copy of the journal cover from page 64
5 copies of the journal page from page 64
access to a stapler

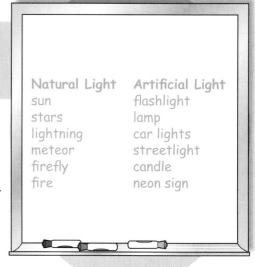

Natural Light	Artificial Light
sun	flashlight
stars	lamp
lightning	car lights
meteor	streetlight
firefly	candle
fire	neon sign

To begin, remind students that there are two types of light sources: *natural* and *artificial* (man-made). Have students brainstorm examples of each type of light as you list their ideas on the board. Then have each child personalize her journal cover and cut it out along with her journal pages. Direct her to stack her journal pages under the cover and staple it at the top.

Observation: For the next five days, have each child use the journal to keep a record of the different light sources she sees. Have her draw each light source on a separate journal page, write its name, and then check the appropriate box. At the end of five days, invite students to share their findings with the class.

The Path of Light

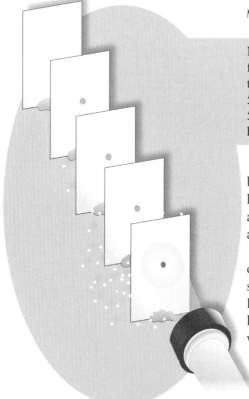

Materials:
flashlight
talcum powder
5 small balls of modeling clay
5 index cards
hole puncher

To prepare, hole-punch the centers of four index cards. Place four small balls of clay about four inches apart in a straight line on a table. Stand one hole-punched card in each ball of clay so that the holes are lined up exactly, as shown. Use a small ball of clay to place the fifth (not hole-punched) card at the end of the row.

Gather students around the cards and darken the room. Direct the beam of the flashlight through the hole in the front card. Ask a volunteer to sprinkle some talcum powder on the beam of light so it is clearly visible. Lead students to determine that the flashlight's beam travels in a straight line through the holes to reflect off the fifth card. Have volunteers predict what will happen if one of the cards is moved slightly left or right. Then move one of the cards and shine the beam through the first card again. Guide students to realize that because light travels in a straight line, when the holes are not lined up, the beam will not reach the fifth card.

Physical Science

Transparent, Translucent, or Opaque?

Materials:
copy of page 65 for each small group
3 empty plastic bottles—one filled with water (Bottle 1), one filled with
    equal parts of milk and water (Bottle 2), and one covered in black
    construction paper (Bottle 3)
flashlight for each small group
variety of objects for testing (see list)

Day 1: Shine a flashlight at the back of each bottle while students observe the front of each bottle. Ask students to identify the bottle through which light can clearly be seen *(Bottle 1)*. Tell students that water is *transparent*, which allows a lot of light to pass through. Next, have students identify the bottle through which light can be seen, but not clearly *(Bottle 2)*. Inform children that the milky water is *translucent*, allowing some light to pass through. Then have students identify the bottle through which no light can be seen *(Bottle 3)*. Explain that the paper is *opaque*, allowing no light to pass through.

Day 2: Review the definitions of *transparent*, *translucent*, and *opaque*. Then place students in groups and give each group a copy of page 65, a flashlight, and four of the objects for testing. Instruct each group to choose an object and draw a picture of it in the box labeled "Object 1." Next, have the group predict whether the object is translucent, transparent, or opaque. Then have one child from each group shine the light on the object and write the test results on the line provided. Have the group repeat the process with the remaining objects.

Objects for Testing
paper plates
lenses from
    sunglasses
waxed paper
tissue paper
different types of
    cups and glasses
plastic wrap
wrapping paper
aluminum foil
colored water

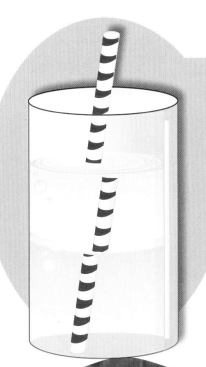

Refraction Action

Materials:
clear glass one-third full of water
clear glass one-third full of cooking oil
2 colored drinking straws

Steps:
1. Place a straw in the glass of water and one in the glass of oil. Invite students to examine the straws from all angles.
2. Pour the oil into the glass of water. (Wait a few seconds for the oil to settle on top of the water.)
3. Have students describe what the straw looks like while looking through the side of the glass. *(The straw appears to be broken in two places.)*
4. Explain that as light passes through substances that have different densities, its speed changes. When the light from the room enters the glass of water and oil, it is refracted, or bent, because the oil and water molecules are different from the molecules in the glass and the air.

Physical Science

Journal Cover and Page Patterns

Use with "Types of Light" on page 62.

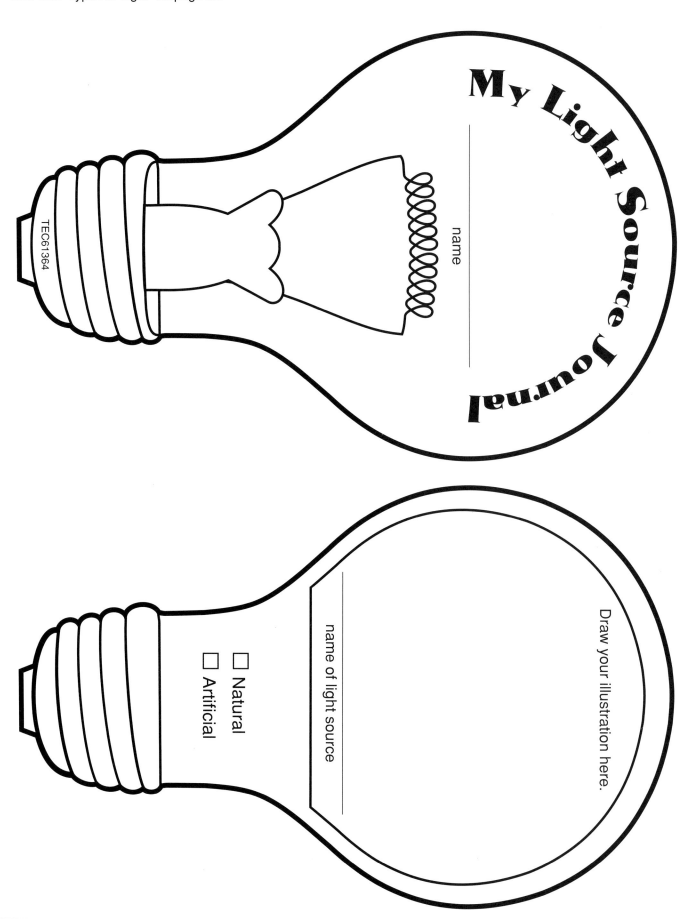

My Light Source Journal

name

TEC61364

Draw your illustration here.

name of light source

☐ Natural
☐ Artificial

20-Minute Science • ©The Mailbox® Books • TEC61364

Object 1

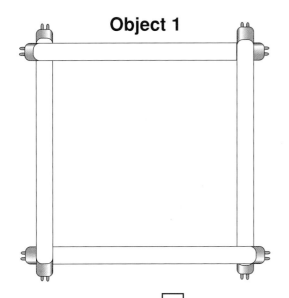

Prediction:
I think this object is... ☐ opaque
☐ translucent
☐ transparent

Results:
This object is _____.

Object 2

Prediction:
I think this object is... ☐ opaque
☐ translucent
☐ transparent

Results:
This object is _____.

Object 3

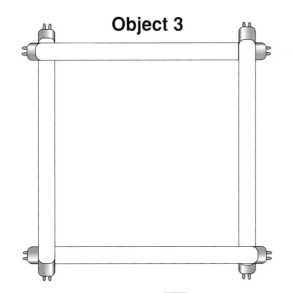

Prediction:
I think this object is... ☐ opaque
☐ translucent
☐ transparent

Results:
This object is _____.

Object 4

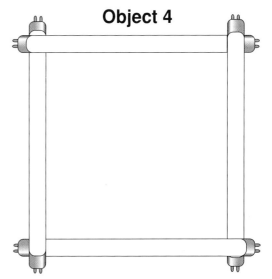

Prediction:
I think this object is... ☐ opaque
☐ translucent
☐ transparent

Results:
This object is _____.

Note to the teacher: Use with "Transparent, Translucent, or Opaque?" on page 63.

Sound

Listen to the Sounds

Materials:
variety of indoor and outdoor sound clips (such as a doorbell chime, a phone ringing, pots clanging, a car horn, and a lawn mower)
chart paper

Invite students to close their eyes and listen as you play the sound clips for them. Then ask students to identify the sounds they heard as you write their responses on a chart. Play the sounds again and compare the actual sounds with those listed on the chart. Guide students in correctly identifying each sound. Discuss with students that some sounds are difficult to recognize without seeing the context in which the sounds are being made.

Tip: Technological resources such as the Internet and online music stores are great places to find appropriate sound clips.

Sound in Motion

Materials for each student:
plastic ruler

Explain to students that all sounds are produced by vibrations or the rapid back and forth movement of an object. Then have each child place a ruler on the edge of a desk and hold it firmly with one hand. Direct her to use the other hand to bend the ruler down and let it go. Have each child observe the ruler's vibrations and listen to the sound it produces. Then instruct her to slide the ruler back on the desk so less of the ruler hangs off the edge and repeat the process. Discuss with students the difference in frequency of vibration and pitch, or highness and lowness of sound, between the two experiments. Guide students to realize that the shorter length of ruler produces quicker vibrations and higher sounds.

Physical Science

Instrument Sounds

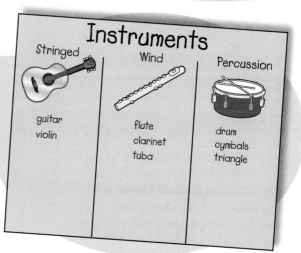

Materials:
class supply of page 69
sound clip of instrumental music
chart, labeled as shown

Day 1: Introduce students to three categories of instruments: stringed, wind, and percussion. Explain that these musical instruments use vibrations to make sounds. Have your students close their eyes as you play the sound clip. Challenge students to name an instrument they remember hearing as you list their ideas in the appropriate columns of the chart.

Day 2: Review the categories of instruments. Point to the chart and review examples of each type of instrument. Then have each child complete a copy of page 69, using the chart as a reference as needed.

Did You Know?
The strings on a guitar vibrate when plucked, blowing across the mouthpiece of a flute causes vibrations inside it, and striking a drum causes vibrations.

Sound Waves

Materials:
Slinky
7 marbles
several dominoes

Explain to students that sound waves occur when a vibrating object causes the surrounding solid, liquid, or gas to vibrate, creating a series of back-and-forth movements. Simulate the rippling movement of sound waves by performing one or more of the following demonstrations:

- **Slinky Stretch**—Have two students each hold a different end of an outstretched Slinky. Direct one student to push his end of the Slinky up and down to send a wave to the other end.

- **Marble Mash**—Place six marbles close together in a line. Have a student roll another marble into the last marble in line. This will cause each marble to hit the one next to it and roll.

- **Domino Dance**—Set up a row of dominoes close together. Ask a student to push over the first domino. Direct your students to watch how the wave travels down the line of dominoes.

Did You Know?
Energy from vibrations stirs up surrounding air molecules, allowing the sound wave to spread out away from the source of the vibration.

Physical Science

Sound

Traveling Sound

Materials for each small group:
plastic comb
transparent container of water

Have each group sit around a separate desk. Remind students that sound can travel through almost any substance; then have each group hypothesize which medium (solid, liquid, or gas) sound will travel through best. Ask a student in each group to strum the teeth of the comb with his thumb while the group listens. Next, direct a student to strum the comb against the edge of the desk as another student listens by placing his ear against the desk. Finally, have a student strum the comb underwater as another student listens with one ear pressed against the container.

Have each group decide which medium sound traveled best in. *(Sound travels faster through solids, so strumming the comb against the edge of the desk should have produced the best sound.)* Guide students to understand that the denser a substance is, the quicker sound will travel through it.

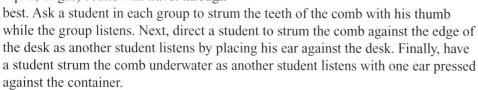

Sound Levels

Leaves rustling	10 decibels
Whispering	20 decibels
Quiet library	30 decibels
Talking	40 decibels
Quiet street	50 decibels
Loud voice	60 decibels
Telephone ringing	70 decibels
Vacuum cleaner	80 decibels
Traffic	90 decibels
Jackhammer	100 decibels
Siren	110 decibels
Racecar	120 decibels

How Loud?

Materials:
class supply of page 70
brass fastener for each child
chart similar to the one shown

Post the chart. Explain to students that sound intensity is measured in decibel units ranging from zero (the weakest sound humans can hear) to 160 (the threshold of pain begins at 140). Review the chart with students, discussing the intensity of each sound. Then have each child cut out the cards on her copy of page 70. Direct her to use the chart as needed to glue the cards from the quietest sound to the loudest sound. Then have her cut out the arrow and attach it to her page with a brass fastener.

Observation: Encourage each child to adjust her arrow throughout the day as she hears sounds of different intensities.

Physical Science

Name

Places, Please!

Cut out the pictures. Glue each one in the correct instrumental section according to the way they make sound.

Percussion instruments make sound when hit or shaken.
Wind instruments use air to make sound.
Stringed instruments make sound when strings vibrate.

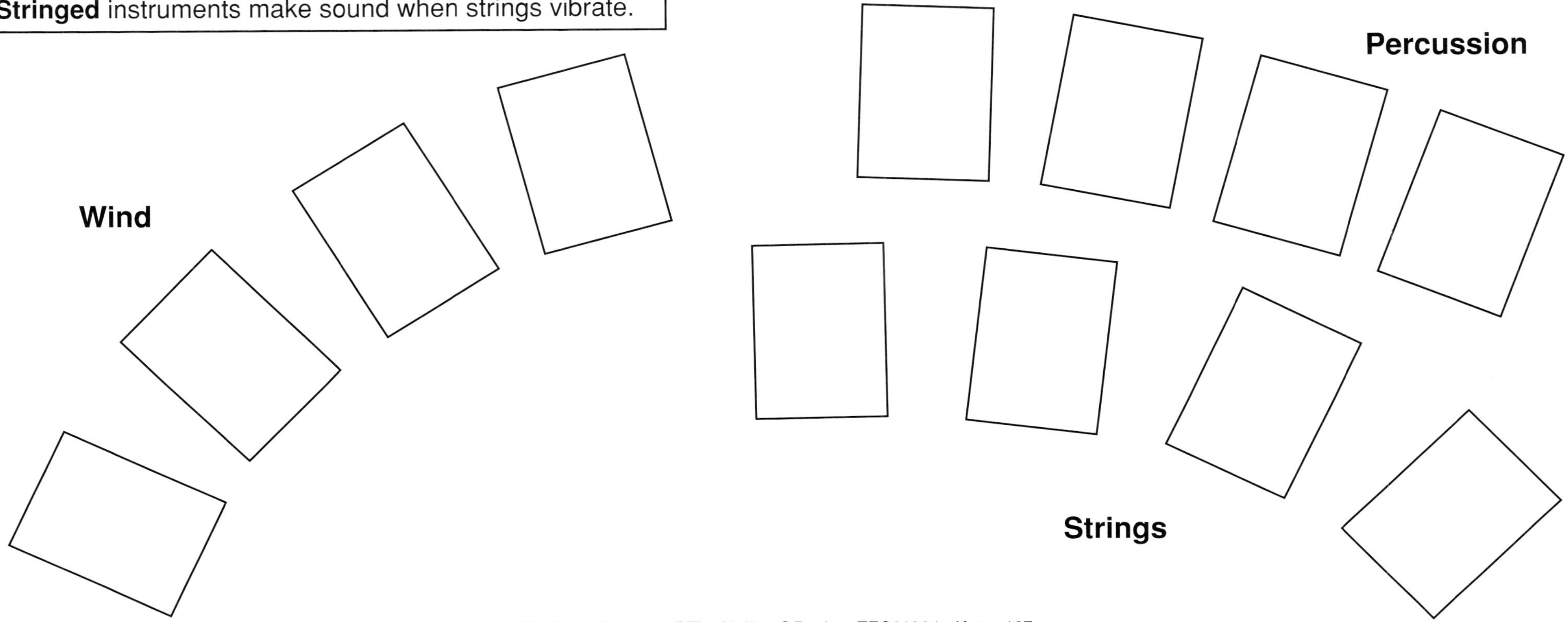

Percussion

Strings

Wind

20-Minute Science • ©The Mailbox® Books • TEC61364 • Key p.127

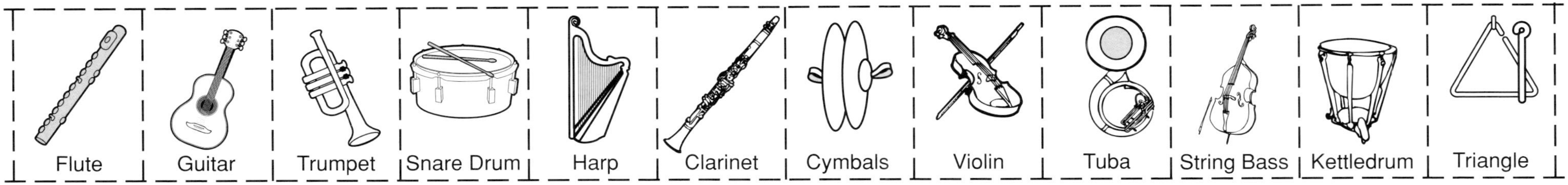

| Flute | Guitar | Trumpet | Snare Drum | Harp | Clarinet | Cymbals | Violin | Tuba | String Bass | Kettledrum | Triangle |

Note to the teacher: Use with "Instrument Sounds" on page 67.

Name

Sound Off!

Listen for directions.

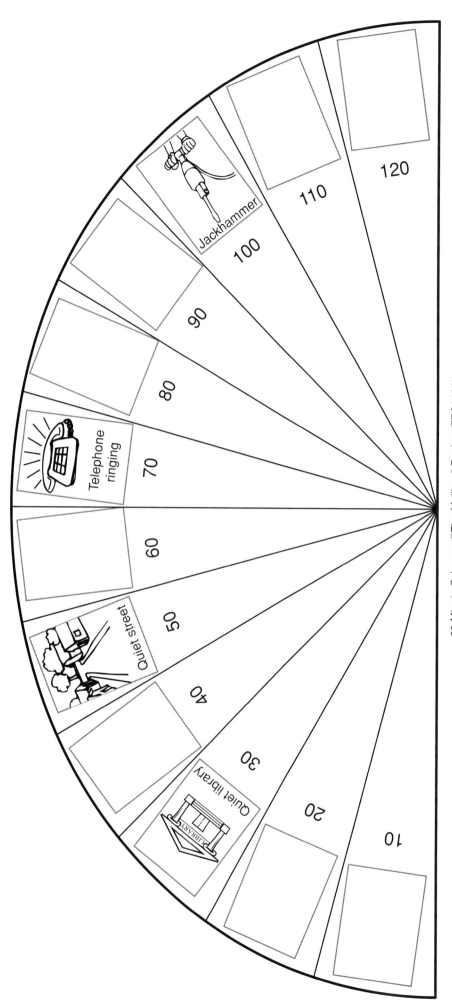

The wheel shows sound levels: 10, 20, 30 (Quiet library), 40, 50 (Quiet street), 60, 70 (Telephone ringing), 80, 90, 100 (Jackhammer), 110, 120.

20-Minute Science • ©The Mailbox® Books • TEC61364

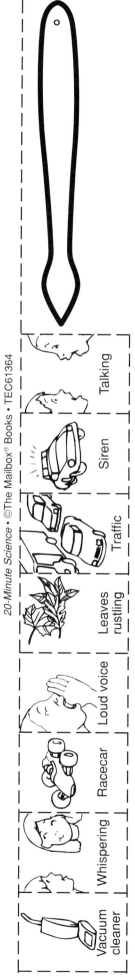

| Vacuum cleaner | Whispering | Racecar | Loud voice | Leaves rustling | Traffic | Siren | Talking |

Note to the teacher: Use with "How Loud?" on page 68.

Matter

Sorting Matter

Materials for each student:
copy of page 74

Remind students that all objects consist of matter and take up space. Then tell students that matter can be described by naming its properties, such as size, shape, texture, color, and temperature. Brainstorm with students different ways the dessert cards could be sorted. Then have each child sort his dessert cards into two categories. Direct him to glue each set of cards to a separate bakery counter and write his categories on the appropriate lines.

Different Ways To
Classify Desserts

circle / not a circle
square / not a square
triangle / not a triangle
chocolate / not chocolate
hard (crunchy) / soft
topping / no topping
fruit / no fruit

Property Practice

It is long and bumpy.
It is yellow.
It is not very heavy,
but it is hard.

A ruler!

Materials for each student:
lunch-size brown paper bag

Review with students the different properties of matter. Then have each child secretly put an object from the classroom in his paper bag. Pair students and invite one child in each duo to give clues about his object by describing its physical properties. After his partner guesses what the object is, have the student remove the item from the bag. If his partner is unable to name the object after five guesses, have the child reveal the item. Then invite the other child in the pair to repeat the process with her item.

Physical Science

In the Bag

Materials:
chart, labeled like the one shown
3 resealable quart-size plastic bags
colorful block
tinted water

To prepare, blow air into a bag and quickly seal it. Seal a colorful block in a second bag, and seal tinted water in a third bag. Show students the three bags and have them identify the type of matter represented in each one. Then use the bags to help students discover the answer to each question on the chart. When all the answers are recorded, lead students to conclude that all matter takes up space. Remind students that solids and most liquids are visible but most gases are not, and that liquids and gases change shape easily but solids do not.

Matter	Solid	Liquid	Gas
Does it take up space?	Yes	Yes	Yes
Does it have weight?	Yes	Yes	Yes
Is it visible?	Yes	Yes	No
Can it change shape easily?	No	Yes	Yes

Possible Settings
birthday party
beach
amusement park
movie theater
playground
restaurant

Things Found in the Kitchen

Solids	Liquids	Gases
crackers	water	air
bread	milk	steam
table	juice	nonstick spray
chair	oil	

Solid, Liquid, or Gas?

Materials for each pair of students:
copy of page 75
index card labeled with a different setting (see list)

Remind students that matter can be found in three common forms: solid, liquid, and gas. Challenge students to name something that they have in their kitchens that can change from a solid to a liquid to a gas *(water)*. On the board, make a chart with headings as shown. Ask students to name things found in their kitchens as you list their responses in the appropriate columns. Then give each pair a card and have a child write the setting at the top of the duo's paper. Invite the twosome to brainstorm items found in that setting and then list the items in the appropriate columns.

Physical Science

Changes in Matter

Materials for each student:
copy of page 76

Display a piece of paper as you remind students that paper is a form of matter because it takes up space. Then explain that a change in matter can be either chemical or physical. Crumple the paper into a ball and have students explain how it changed. *(It changed size and shape.)* Reinforce that although the paper changed, it is still paper so the change was a physical change. Then guide students to realize if you burned the paper it would no longer be paper because it would change size, shape, color, texture, and substance. This would result in a chemical change. To conclude, have students complete a copy of page 76 to review other physical and chemical changes.

Did You Know?
A chemical change occurs when the composition of matter changes. A physical change alters the physical properties, but there is no change in the composition.

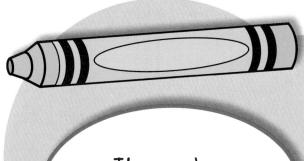

It can be broken in half.

Physical Changes

Materials for each small group:
different sample of solid matter, such as a piece of paper, an apple, a crayon, a ball of clay, or a piece of chalk

After reviewing with students what a physical change is, give each group a sample of matter. Then invite each group to brainstorm possible physical changes for its matter sample. After a predetermined amount of time, invite each group, in turn, to share the possible ways its matter sample could be physically changed. **For an added challenge**, also invite students to brainstorm possible chemical changes (if any) for their matter sample.

Physical Science

Name _____

Delicious Desserts

Desserts for Sale!

Category: _____

Desserts for Sale!

Category: _____

20-Minute Science • ©The Mailbox® Books • TEC61364

doughnut

cookie

ice cream cone

cake slice

turnover

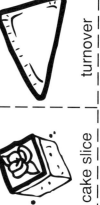

pie slice

frosted brownie

candy apple

Note to the teacher: Use with "Sorting Matter" on page 71.

State Your Matter

Read the setting written on your card.
Brainstorm with your partner different items found in the setting.
Write each item in the correct box.

Setting: _____

Solids	**Liquids**	**Gases**

Note to the teacher: Use with "Solid, Liquid, or Gas?" on page 72.

Check Out the Changes!

When matter changes only in the way it looks or feels, it is a **physical** change. When matter changes to become a new substance, it is a **chemical** change.

Read about each physical or chemical change in matter. Answer each question.

Matter Man

1. You crumple a paper bag into a ball.

   What changes happen? _____

   Is the bag still a bag?_____

   Is this a physical or chemical change? _____

2. You burn an old letter into many pieces.

   What changes happen? _____

   Is the letter still a letter?_____

   Is this a physical or chemical change? _____

3. You cut a sandwich in half.

   What changes happen? _____

   Is the sandwich still a sandwich?_____

   Is this a physical or chemical change? _____

4. A metal toy is left in a puddle of water, and it rusts.

   What changes happen? _____

   Is the metal still a metal?_____

   Is this a physical or chemical change? _____

5. A picture fades after being in the sunlight.

   What changes happen? _____

   Is the picture still a picture?_____

   Is this a physical or chemical change? _____

Bonus: On the back of this paper, draw pictures to show how a candle, a crayon, and a scoop of ice cream can each be changed.

Rocks & Soil

Rock Vocabulary

Review characteristics of rocks with students.
Then lead students in completing this unique vocabulary activity.

Materials for each student:
tagboard copy of page 83
6' length of yarn
tape
access to a hole puncher

Steps for students:

1. Fold the paper in half along the fold line and tape the edges together opposite the fold. Then hole-punch where indicated.
2. Starting from the back of the card, thread the yarn through the hole next to the first vocabulary word on the left side. Tape the end of the yarn to the back of the card.
3. Read the first word on the left side. Then thread the yarn through the hole next to the matching definition on the right side.
4. Continue in this manner with each vocabulary word and definition, working from top to bottom.
5. Check the back of the card to see if your yarn overlaps the lines on the card correctly.

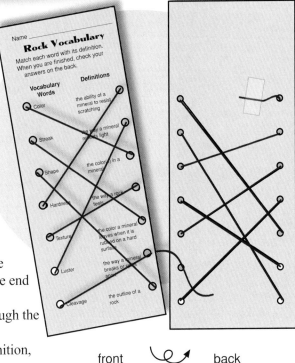

front   back

Rock Report

Materials:

assembled copy of the booklet project on pages 84–86 for each student	butter knives
	glass jar
small rock for each student	vinegar
unglazed ceramic tile	droppers
magnifying glasses	magnets
pennies	container of water

Set up the rock exploration centers as described on page 78. Plan to leave the centers in place for five days. Give a rock to each child. Then invite students to visit one center each day and use the following directions to complete their booklets:

Cover: Draw a picture of your rock in the box.
Page 1: Examine your rock. Complete each sentence.
Pages 2–5: Follow the directions on page 78.

My Rock Report

My rock

Rockologist ___ Cindy

Earth & Space Science

Rock Exploration Centers

Use with "Rock Report" on page 77.

Booklet Page 2–True Colors: Have each child use a streak test to determine the minerals that are present in his rock. To do this, have each student rub his rock across an unglazed ceramic tile. Explain that a small amount of rock is ground off as it is moved across the tile. The streak of color left on the tile's surface is the rock's true color. (If no colored streak is left, the rock is harder than the tile.)

Booklet Page 3–Hard Evidence: Explain to students that a mineral will scratch other minerals softer than itself and will be scratched by minerals that are harder. Place pennies, butter knives, and a glass jar at a center. Have each student try to scratch each item with her rock. Then have her try to scratch her rock with her fingernail, a penny, and a butter knife.

Booklet Page 4–Fizzy Findings: Explain to students that rocks containing limestone will bubble when they come into contact with a weak acid such as vinegar. Place a container of vinegar, droppers, and paper towels at a center. Have each child use a dropper to place a small amount of vinegar on his rock.

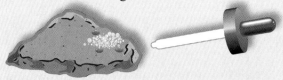

Booklet Page 5–Attractive Rocks: Explain to students that a rock containing metal will be attracted to a magnet. Place several magnets at a center. Have each child touch his rock to a magnet and observe whether he feels a magnetic attraction.

Booklet Page 5–Get Wet!: Set up a center with a container of water and paper towels. Have each youngster drop her rock into the water and observe whether it sinks or floats.

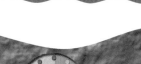

Did You Know?
Pumice will float on water.

Earth & Space Science

Different Types

Materials for each student:
copy of page 87

To begin, review information about igneous, metamorphic, and sedimentary rocks with students. Then give each child a copy of page 87. Have him cut out each word in scrambled sentence 1. Instruct him to arrange the words in the correct order and glue them in place in the appropriate box. Direct him to repeat this process for each scrambled sentence. When his work is complete, have him read each sentence to review information about the three different types of rocks.

Rock Reference

Materials for each student:
4½" x 12" piece of colorful construction paper
copy of pages 88 and 89

Steps for students:
1. Cut out the booklet pages and rock formation cards.
2. Read each rock formation card; then glue it to the matching booklet page.
3. Fold the construction paper to make a booklet cover.
4. Stack the pages in order, slip them inside the cover, and staple them along the left side.
5. Title the booklet "A Rock Reference" and decorate the cover as desired.

Igneous Rock Candy

Materials:
chocolate or butterscotch morsels
glass mixing bowl
spoon

access to a microwave oven
waxed paper

To demonstrate the formation of igneous rocks, have each child place a spoonful of chocolate or butterscotch morsels into the bowl. Microwave the morsels on high for 20 seconds or until they can be stirred with a spoon. Have students compare the unmelted chips to the melted chips. Then, for each child, drop a spoonful of the mixture (melted rock) onto a sheet of waxed paper. As the rocks cool, lead students in discussing the similarities between the experiment and the formation of igneous rocks. Once the treats have cooled and hardened, invite each child to enjoy her igneous rock.

Did You Know?
Igneous rock is formed when melted rock, called magma, pushes through cracks in the earth's crust in the form of lava and then cools and solidifies.

Earth & Space Science

Metamorphic Gumdrops

Have each child make a metamorphic rock as described below. Then explain to students that, in a similar manner, rocks can be changed into new rocks by the weight of the earth's layers pressing down on them.

Materials for each student:
5 gumdrops in assorted colors, each cut into pieces (rocks)
two 5" squares of waxed paper

Steps for students:
1. Pile the gumdrop pieces in the center of one waxed paper square.
2. Lay the second waxed paper square on top of the pile.
3. Use your palm to press down on the gumdrop pieces for several seconds.
4. Peel the waxed paper off to reveal a colorful metamorphic rock.

Layers Upon Layers

Follow the steps below to model for students the layering process of the formation of sedimentary rocks.

Materials:

plastic quart jar with lid	½ c. dry rice
plastic widemouthed jar	½ c. dry pinto beans
½ c. flour	2 c. water

Steps:
1. Pour one cup of water into the quart jar and add the beans, rice, and flour. Then add the second cup of water.
2. Tightly screw the lid onto the jar and have volunteers take turns shaking the jar vigorously for five to ten minutes.
3. Pour the contents into the widemouthed jar.
4. Invite students to discuss their observations.

Observation:

Encourage students to examine the contents of the jar every 15 minutes for about an hour. Invite students to share what they see happening. *(The water will be cloudy until the mixture begins to settle. As it settles, three layers will become visible: a layer of beans and rice, a layer of flour, and a layer of dirty-looking water. Some of the flour will drift down to fill in the spaces in the layer of rice and beans.)* Leave the jar in an undisturbed location overnight. Have students examine the jar the next day and share their observations.

Earth & Space Science

Everyday Minerals

Materials:
chart with headings, similar to the one shown

Lead students in a discussion about how important and useful minerals are, giving several examples. *(Gold and diamonds are used in jewelry, and graphite is used to make pencil lead.)* Post the chart. Then have students brainstorm items made from the minerals on the chart as you list their ideas in the appropriate sections.

Minerals

Magnetite	Gold
magnets	necklace
	ring
	electronics
Aluminum	**Copper**
can	pipes
pots	wire
pans	penny
foil	

Made From Rocks or Minerals

Not Made From Rocks or Minerals

Rocks at Work

Materials:
drill bit
drinking glass
filled salt shaker
container of paint
piece of chalk
piece of paper
book
rubber eraser
2 sentence strips, labeled as shown

Show students each item, in turn, and lead them in discussing the products that make up each object. Then place the sentence strips on a surface in front of students. Ask a volunteer to choose an item and place it under the appropriate heading as he explains his reasoning. Continue in this manner with the remaining items. Then invite student volunteers to name additional items and say whether they are made from rocks or minerals or not made from rocks or minerals.

Earth & Space Science

Soil Formation

Materials for each student:
copy of page 90
assembled booklet made from 5 half sheets of construction paper

Review with students where soil comes from and how it is formed. Then lead students in completing the booklet project below.

Steps for students:
1. Title the booklet "Soil Is Formed" and decorate the front cover as desired.
2. Cut out the picture and description cards.
3. For each picture card, find the matching description card.
4. Glue each pair onto a different booklet page.

Did You Know?
Soil is the product formed when rocks break down and mix with water, air, and rotting organic material.

Finding Fossils

Materials for each student:
copy of page 91

Explain to students that the Grand Canyon (in Arizona) is one of the most famous scenic wonders in the United States because of its age and immense size. Further explain that billions of years ago, the rocks at the bottom of the Grand Canyon were an ocean floor. Tell students that over the years, layers of sandstone, shale, and limestone have built up on top of the floor. Over time, the rushing of the Colorado River has worn away the stone, revealing the changes that have occurred in the earth's surface over the last two billion years and fossils hidden in the canyon's rocks. To illustrate this, have each student follow the directions on her copy of page 91.

Earth & Space Science

Name _____

Rock Vocabulary

Match each word with its definition. When you are finished, check your answers on the back.

Vocabulary Words	Definitions
● Color	● the ability of a mineral to resist scratching
● Streak	● the way a mineral reflects light
● Shape	● the color(s) in a mineral
● Hardness	● the way a rock feels
● Texture	● the color a mineral leaves when it is rubbed on a hard surface
● Luster	● the way a mineral breaks or splits apart
● Cleavage	● the outline of a rock

Fold here.

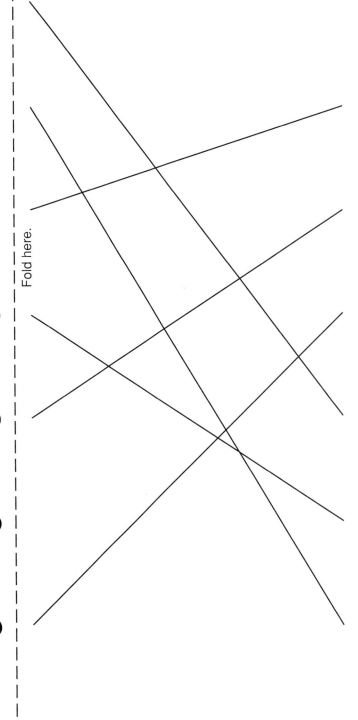

Note to the teacher: Use with "Rock Vocabulary" on page 77.

My Rock Report

My rock

Rockologist _____

20-Minute Science • ©The Mailbox® Books • TEC61364

Take a Closer Look

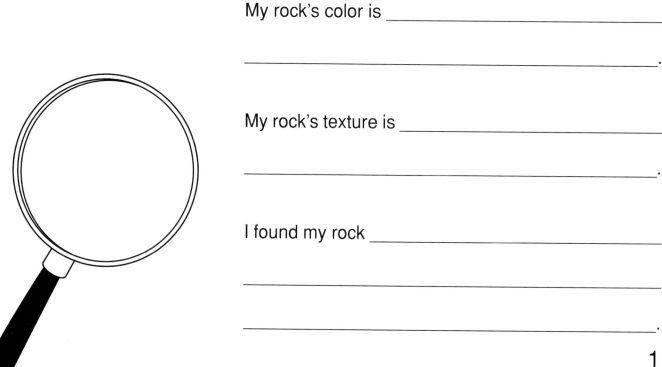

My rock's color is _____

_____.

My rock's texture is _____

_____.

I found my rock _____

_____

_____.

1

Note to the teacher: Use with "Rock Report" on page 77.

True Colors

☐ My rock did not leave a streak.

☐ My rock did leave a streak.

The streak color was _____.

My rock's streak color looked like this:

2

Hard Evidence

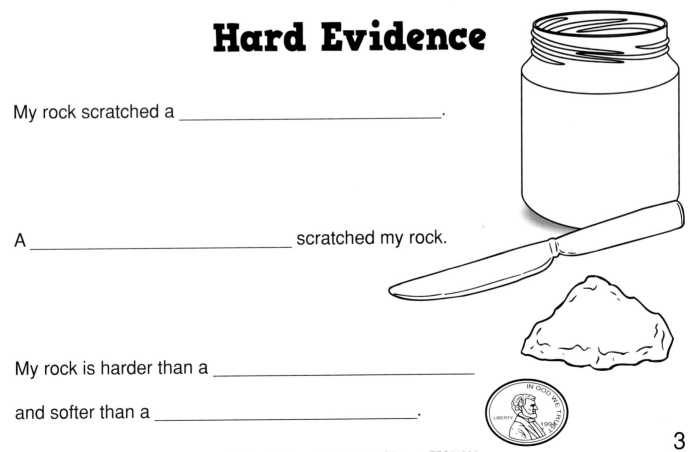

My rock scratched a _____.

A _____ scratched my rock.

My rock is harder than a _____

and softer than a _____.

3

20-Minute Science • ©The Mailbox® Books • TEC61364

Note to the teacher: Use with "Rock Report" on page 77.

Fizzy Findings

My rock looked like this when I put vinegar on it.

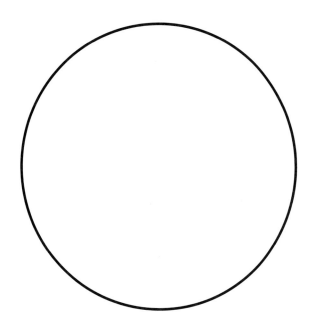

My rock _____ fizz.
(did or did not)

My rock _____
(does or does not)

contain limestone.

4

Attractive Rocks

My rock _____ cling to a magnet.
(did or did not)

I learned _____

_____

_____.

Get Wet!

My rock _____.
(sinks or floats)

5

20-Minute Science • ©The Mailbox® Books • TEC61364

Note to the teacher: Use with "Rock Report" on page 77.

Scrambled Rock Sentences

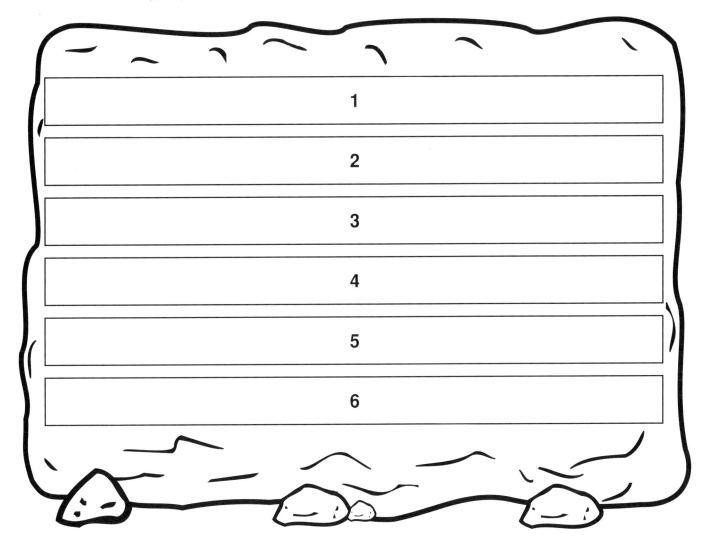

1									
1	forms	Igneous	cools	rock	and	hardens.	magma	when	
2	most	is	Basalt	igneous	the	rock.	common		
3	layers	from	sediment.	rock	Sedimentary	forms	of		
4	type	rock.	Sandstone	of	one	sedimentary	is		
5	pressure.	rocks	forms	heat	are	Metamorphic	when	by	and/or	rock	changed
6	type	rock.	is	metamorphic	Marble	a	of			

Note to the teacher: Use with "Different Types" on page 79.

Booklet Pages
Use with "Rock Reference" on page 79.

Igneous Rock

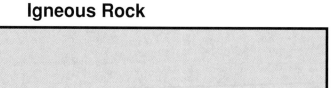

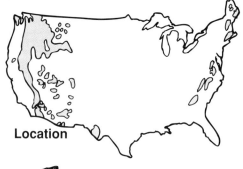

Location

Facts About Igneous Rock

- There are two classifications of igneous rock: *extrusive* and *intrusive.*
- Extrusive rock forms on the earth's surface.
- Intrusive rock forms beneath the earth's surface.

Basalt   **Pumice**   **Obsidian**   **Granite**

Metamorphic Rock

Metamorphic Rock

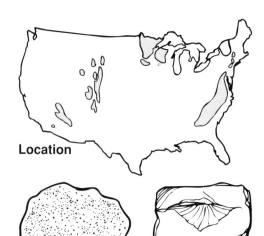

Location

Facts About Metamorphic Rock

- Granite can be changed into gneiss.
- Limestone can be changed into marble.
- Sandstone can be changed into quartzite.

Marble   **Slate**   **Quartzite**   **Gneiss**

20-Minute Science • ©The Mailbox® Books • TEC61364 • Key p. 128

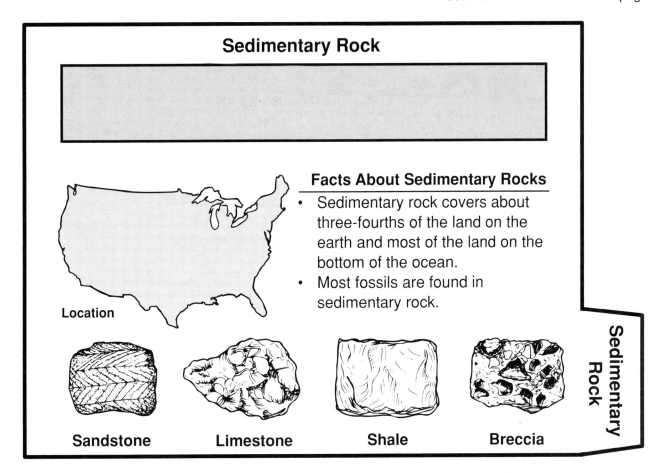

Sedimentary Rock

Facts About Sedimentary Rocks
- Sedimentary rock covers about three-fourths of the land on the earth and most of the land on the bottom of the ocean.
- Most fossils are found in sedimentary rock.

Location

Sandstone   Limestone   Shale   Breccia

Sedimentary Rock

Rock Formation Cards

This type of rock forms when heat or pressure or both cause changes in the other two types of rock.

This type of rock forms when molten material, or magma, cools and hardens.

This type of rock forms when small pieces of clay, silt, or sand settle into layers on the bottoms of lakes and oceans. The pressure of the water and the layers above compress the pieces into rock.

Booklet Picture and Description Cards

Use with "Soil Formation" on page 82.

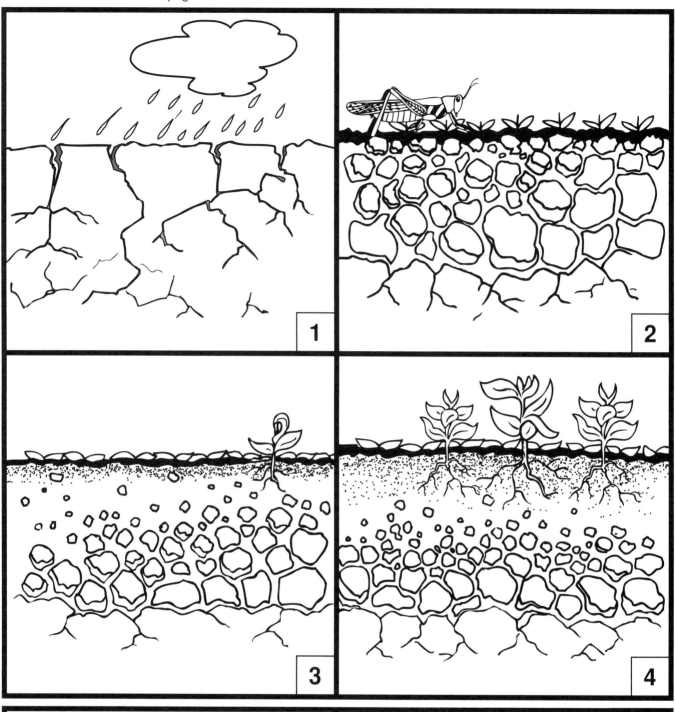

Finally, the soil is healthy and able to grow plants.	Soil begins to form when weather and other natural forces break down rocks and other substances. TEC61364
Once the rocks begin to break down, plantlike matter and animal matter help them continue to break down.	Different layers, or *horizons,* begin to show in the soil.

Name

Grand Layers of Rock

Use the key to help you label each rock layer in the blank.
Color each rock layer. Use the color code at the bottom of the page.

Key

shark teeth (limestone)

clams (limestone)

scorpion tracks (sandstone)

reptile tracks (sandstone)

insect wings (shale)

land plants (shale)

ferns (shale or sandstone)

bony fish plates (limestone)

earlier shelled animals (shale)

Color Code
limestone = gray
sandstone = yellow
shale = brown
shale or sandstone = red

20-Minute Science • ©The Mailbox® Books • TEC61364 • Key p. 128

Note to the teacher: Use with "Finding Fossils" on page 82.

Weather

Weather Observations

Materials for each student:
5-page booklet with construction paper covers, similar to the one shown

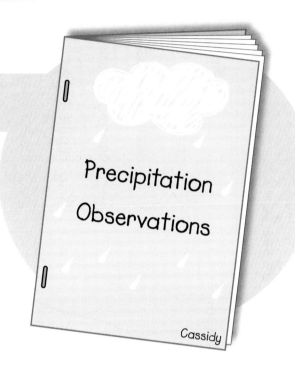

Review with students the four basic types of precipitation: rain, snow, sleet, and hail. Then have students brainstorm words that describe the various types of precipitation as you list their ideas on the board. Give each child a booklet and have her title it as shown. Invite her to decorate the cover as desired.

Observation: On each of the next five days that precipitation occurs, have each child write the date on a page of her booklet. Then have her write to describe the precipitation and add a matching illustration.

Precipitation...

- helps crops grow

- can cause cancellations

- provides drinking water

- can cause floods

- makes the grass green

Effects of Precipitation

Materials:
chart paper
several large sheets of paper

Day 1: Share information about different types of precipitation with students. Then have students brainstorm the effects of precipitation as you list their ideas on a sheet of chart paper. Discuss with students which effects are positive and which are negative.

Day 2: Review with students the information discussed on Day 1. Then divide students into small groups. Assign each group a condition, such as no rain or heavy rain for months. Direct the students in each group to label a sheet of paper with their assigned condition. Have them brainstorm possible effects of the condition and list them on their paper. If time permits, invite each group to share its work with the class.

Earth & Space Science

Weather Word Wheel

Materials:
class supply of page 100
class supply of brads
die for every 2 students

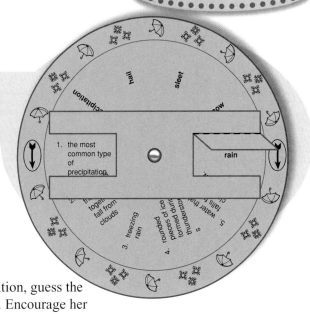

Day 1: After reviewing the different types of precipitation with students, have each child cut out her wheel pattern. Then direct each student to cut along the bold lines of the window strip pattern and fold the window flap up at the dashed line. Have her use a brad to attach the window strip pattern atop the wheel. For vocabulary practice, have her turn the wheel in the direction indicated until the first definition is revealed. Have her silently read the definition, guess the corresponding word, and then lift the flap to check her answer. Encourage her to continue with the remaining words and definitions.

Day 2: Review the vocabulary from the wheel pattern with students. Then pair students and give each duo a die. Instruct one child in each twosome to roll the die. Have her turn the wheel so that the definition with the same number is shown in the window. (If she rolls a six, have her turn the wheel to a definition of her choosing.) The student reads the definition to her partner. After the partner guesses the word, the first child lifts the flap to check the answer. Have the partners switch roles and take turns in this manner.

Rain, Rain, Rain!

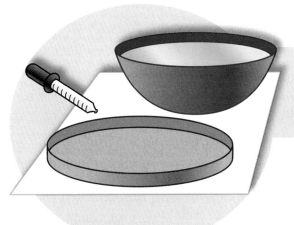

Materials for each pair of students:
eyedropper
plastic lid
small container of water
paper towel

Lead students through this experiment to find out why, if all clouds contain water, it doesn't rain more often. Direct one student in each twosome to use the eyedropper to make water droplets on the plastic lid. As his partner watches closely, have the child quickly turn the lid over and hold it above the paper towel. After the students observe what happens, have them dry the lid, switch roles, and repeat the process. After each duo has finished, invite students to share their observations. Lead them to conclude that only the large drops fell from the plastic lid. Explain that, similarly, only the heavy droplets in a cloud fall. Tiny droplets must combine with other droplets to increase their weight before they fall.

Did You Know?
It takes more than one million cloud droplets to make a single raindrop.

Earth & Space Science

Frosty Figures

Materials for each student:
copy of page 101
6" x 18" sheet of construction paper
chart like the one shown

Explain to students that a snowflake's shape is determined by where the snowflake is formed and the temperature of the clouds it travels through as it falls. Share the information on the chart with students. Then have them follow the directions below to make a booklet.

Steps for students:

1. Use the word bank to complete each sentence on page 101. Write your name on the title card.
2. Accordion-fold the construction paper into four equal-size sections as shown. Keep the paper folded.
3. Cut out the cards on page 101. Glue the title card to the front of the booklet.
4. Unfold the paper. Glue a snowflake card on each section and glue the matching description below it.

Snowflakes

Where Formed	Shape	Illustration
high clouds	capped columns	
middle clouds	hexagonal plates	
low clouds	starlike crystals, needles, hexagonal plates	

Did You Know?
All snowflakes have six sides, but no two are exactly alike!

Water Cycle

Materials:
copy of page 102
chart paper

Ask students to brainstorm how they think water gets in the clouds to fall as precipitation. List their ideas on chart paper. Then draw and label a simple sketch on the board to review the water cycle with students. Explain that the water cycle gets its name from the circle it travels in. Then lead students to conclude that rain is caused by water evaporating into the clouds. To further review the water cycle, have each child complete his copy of page 102.

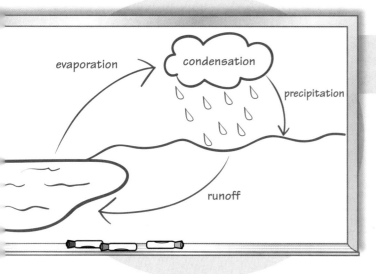

Earth & Space Science

Artificial Wind

Materials for each student:
balloon

This simple activity helps students understand how wind is created. To begin, explain to students that wind is produced when an area of cooler, heavier air rushes into an area of warmer, low-pressure air. Then have each student blow up her balloon and pinch the opening to keep the air inside. Instruct each child to feel the side of her balloon. Ask students if they think the high-pressure air is inside or outside the balloon. Guide students to realize that the high-pressure air is inside the balloon. Direct each child to place her hand near the opening of the balloon and then release the air inside. Lead students to realize that the wind they feel is caused by the high-pressure air inside the balloon rushing into the low-pressure air outside the balloon.

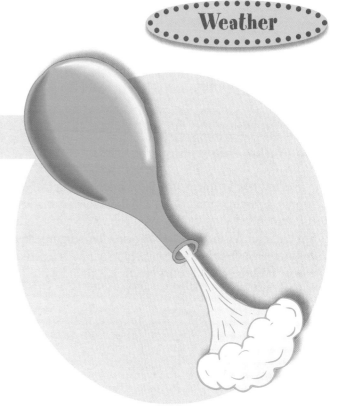

Measuring Wind Speed

Materials for each pair of students:
tagboard copy of page 103
1½" foam ball
7½" length of thread
tape
unsharpened pencil

Steps for students:
1. Cut out the anemometer pattern and recording strip.
2. Tape the anemometer pattern to the pencil as shown.
3. Tape one end of the thread to the foam ball and the opposite end to the corner of the pattern, making sure the thread falls across the zero mark.

Observation: Each day for a week, take students outside. Instruct one child from each pair to face the wind while he points the arrow on the anemometer away from him. Have the other student record where the string crosses the scale in the appropriate box on the duo's recording strip. After one week of testing, discuss the results with students to determine which days were breeziest and which were calmer.

Did You Know?
An anemometer is an instrument used by scientists to measure how fast air moves.

Earth & Space Science

Types of Clouds

Materials:
song poster similar to the one shown
class supply of cloud cutouts

Review with students the three main families of clouds (stratus, cumulus, and cirrus) and their characteristics. Then lead students in singing the song, each time substituting different cloud words in the chorus. After singing, have each child write on his cloud cutout a fact that he learned about clouds. Post the cutouts on a blue background with the title "Among the Clouds."

Did You Know?
Clouds form as water vapor rises and condenses into liquid.

I Know What Cloud That Must Be
(sung to the tune of "My Bonnie Lies Over the Ocean")

Verse:
I see clouds in the sky stretched like blankets.
I see clouds in the sky looking gray.
I see clouds in the sky bringing raindrops.
Those are stratus clouds I see today.
Chorus:
Must be, must be,
Those must be stratus clouds I see, I see.
Must be, must be,
Those must be stratus clouds I see.
Verse:
I see clouds in the sky that look puffy.
I see clouds in the sky that are fat.
I see clouds that look just like cotton.
Those are cumulus clouds I'd like to pat!
Chorus: cumulus
Verse:
I see clouds in the sky that look wispy.
I see clouds in the sky that look thin.
I see clouds that look just like feathers.
Those are cirrus clouds I see again.
Chorus: cirrus

Making a Cloud

Follow the steps below to demonstrate for students one way clouds form.

Materials:
12" x 18" sheet of dark-colored construction paper
clear jar
pitcher of hot water
pie tin
enough ice cubes to fill the pie tin

Steps:
1. Pour the hot water in the jar until it is three-fourths full.
2. Put the jar in front of the construction paper. (This makes the clouds easier to see.)
3. Put the ice in the pie tin and place it atop the jar of hot water.
4. Watch the cloud appear. Explain to students that as the warm, moist air in the jar meets the cold air at the top, it cools. It is unable to hold all the water vapor, so some of it condenses.

Did You Know?
As warm air rises, it carries water vapor. As the water vapor rises, it cools and changes back to water droplets, which gather together to form clouds.

Earth & Space Science

Can Clouds

Materials:
2 empty smooth-sided cans
ice cubes
paper towels

To demonstrate how clouds are made, fill one can with ice to chill it. Have students take turns rubbing the other can between their hands for two minutes to warm it up. Remove the ice cubes from the first can. Exhale on the cool can and show the resulting moisture to the group. Then exhale on the warm can and show the results. Lead students to realize that there is more moisture on the cold can. Explain that this is because warm, moist exhaled air contains water vapor that condenses onto the cold can's cooler surface, leaving tiny droplets of water. The water vapor from exhaled air on the warm can evaporates quickly or doesn't condense at all.

Condensation Demonstration

Materials:
2 clear drinking glasses
warm water
ice water

Model the process of condensation for students with this demonstration. To begin, half-fill one glass with warm water and the other with ice water. Have students watch the glasses for three minutes. Then have each child touch the outside of each glass. Explain to students that the water vapor in the air touches the cold water glass and is cooled. It condenses, making the outside of the glass wet. Droplets don't form on the warm water glass because the air around it is not cooled.

Earth & Space Science

Fogging Up

Materials:
pair of eyeglasses
ice cubes in a covered pan

Tell students that fog is made up of tiny water droplets, just as clouds are. To demonstrate to students how fog is formed, place the eyeglasses in the pan of ice and recover it. Wait two minutes and then remove the glasses and ask students to observe the lenses. Guide students to realize that the lenses fog up because the warmer air in the room condenses on the colder surface of the glass lenses.

Did You Know?
Fog is a cloud near the earth's surface.

Cozy Cloud Blankets

Materials:
2 clear 16 oz. jars
2 thermometers
large handful of cotton batting
watch
warm water

Discuss with students whether they think cloudy or clear nights are cooler. Then use this simple demonstration to show students how clouds form a natural blanket around the earth.

Steps:
1. Half-fill each jar with hot water.
2. Place a thermometer in each jar. After several minutes, record each thermometer's temperature on the board. Then cover one jar with the batting (clouds).
3. Check and record each jar's temperature at 5- and 10-minute intervals.
4. Compare and discuss the results with students. Guide students to conclude that the batting, like clouds over the earth's surface, helps keep heat in the jar. This makes clear nights cooler than cloudy nights because there is no blanket of clouds to hold the heat near the earth's surface.

Earth & Space Science

Stormy Words

Materials for each student:
tagboard copy of page 104

Have each child cut out the television pattern, word strip, and definition strip on his copy of page 104. Instruct him to carefully cut along the two sets of dashed lines on the television screen. Then have him gently thread the definition strip through the top slots and the word strip through the bottom slots, as shown. Have him pull the strips to match each word, in turn, to its definition.

The Eye of a Storm

Use this demonstration to show students what it is like in the eye of a hurricane.

Materials:

large, clear mixing bowl, filled three-fourths full of water
black pepper
wooden spoon

plastic ruler
length of string
paper clip
tape

Steps:
1. Tie one end of the string to the paper clip.
2. Tape the other end of the string to the underside of the ruler. Adjust the string until the paper clip is hanging on a length that is one inch shorter than the depth of the water in the bowl. Set the ruler aside.
3. Sprinkle a generous amount of pepper in the water.
4. Stir the water until it is swirling.
5. Quickly lower the paper clip into the center of the bowl until the ruler rests on its edges.
6. Lead the class in discussing the results. *(The water will continue to swirl around. However, the paper clip will move only gently, or not at all. Explain to students that, in the same way, the air inside the eye of a hurricane remains calm while winds swirl around it.)*

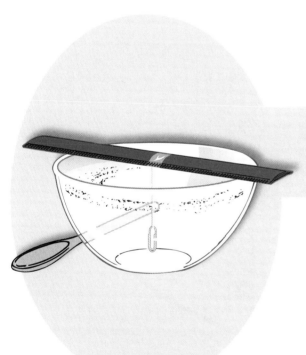

See the cloud journal skill sheet on page 105.

Earth & Space Science

Wheel and Window Strip Patterns

Use with "Weather Word Wheel" on page 93.

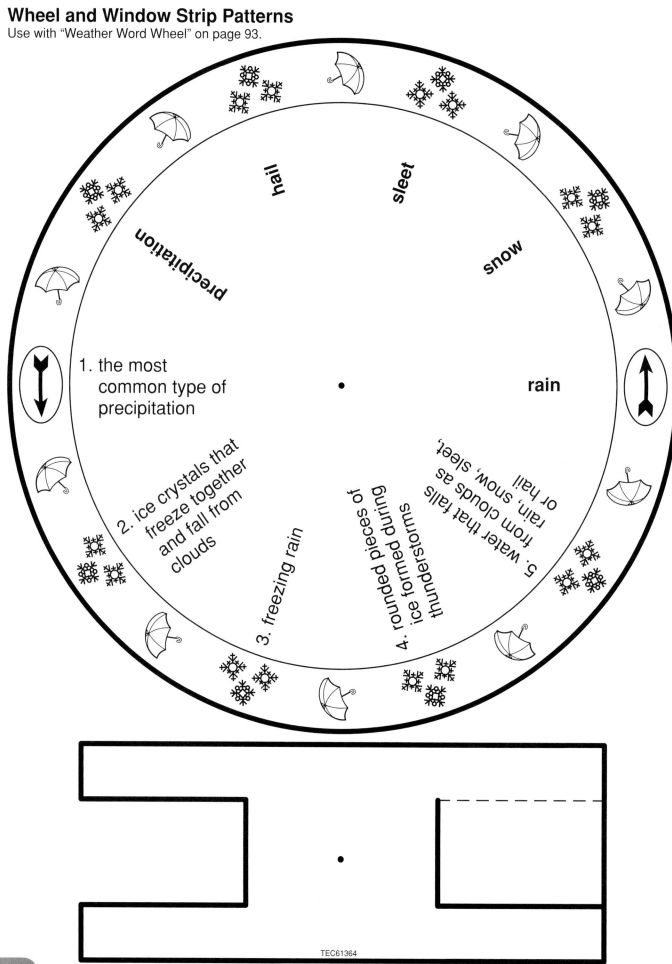

The most common type of precipitation

1. the most common type of precipitation

2. ice crystals that freeze together and fall from clouds

3. freezing rain

4. rounded pieces of ice formed during thunderstorms

5. water that falls from clouds as rain, snow, sleet, or hail

precipitation

hail

sleet

snow

rain

TEC61364

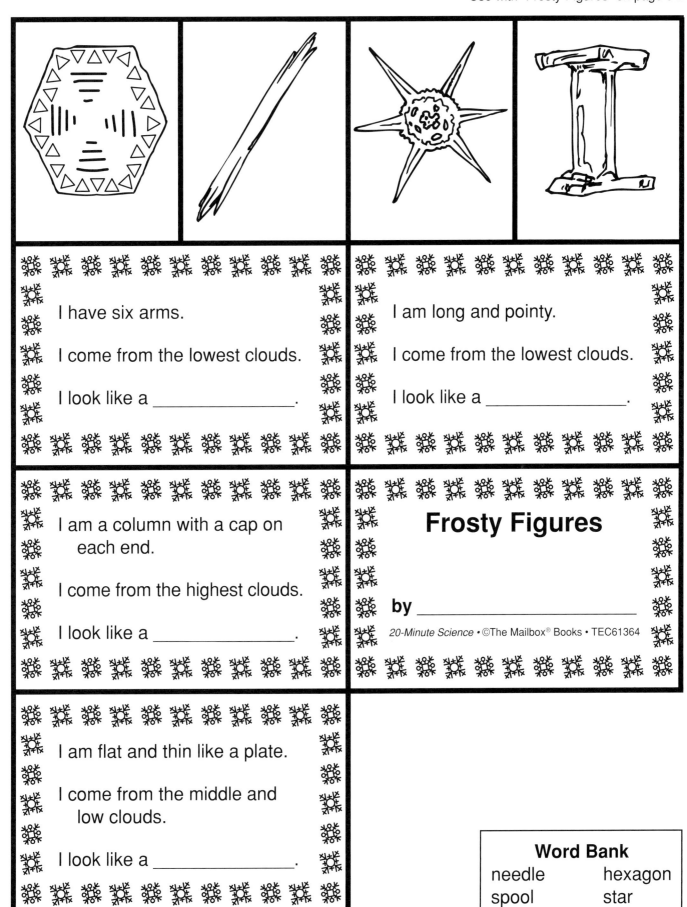

I have six arms.

I come from the lowest clouds.

I look like a _____.

I am long and pointy.

I come from the lowest clouds.

I look like a _____.

I am a column with a cap on each end.

I come from the highest clouds.

I look like a _____.

Frosty Figures

by _____

20-Minute Science • ©The Mailbox® Books • TEC61364

I am flat and thin like a plate.

I come from the middle and low clouds.

I look like a _____.

Word Bank
needle   hexagon
spool   star

Water Cycle

Cut out the cards.
Glue them in the correct location.

20-Minute Science • ©The Mailbox® Books • TEC61364 • Key p.128

Precipitation	Condensation	Evaporation	Runoff

Note to the teacher: Use with "Water Cycle" on page 94.

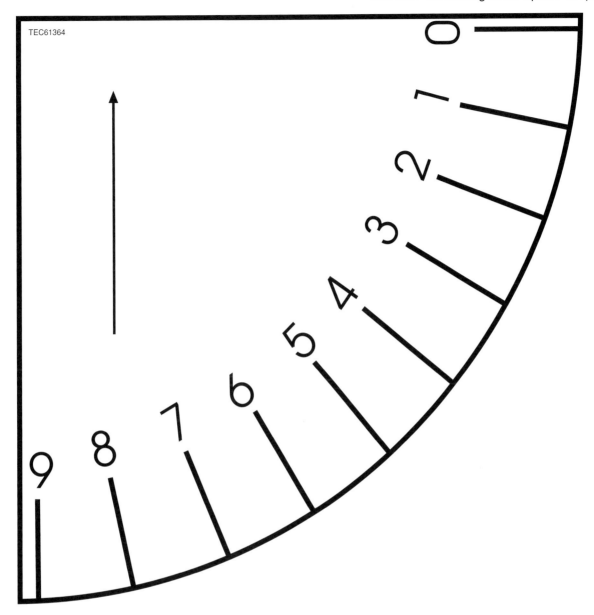

TEC61364

0
1
2
3
4
5
6
7
8
9

Name				
Record of Wind Speed				
Monday	Tuesday	Wednesday	Thursday	Friday

Television Pattern, Word Strip, and Definition Strip

Use with "Stormy Words" on page 99.

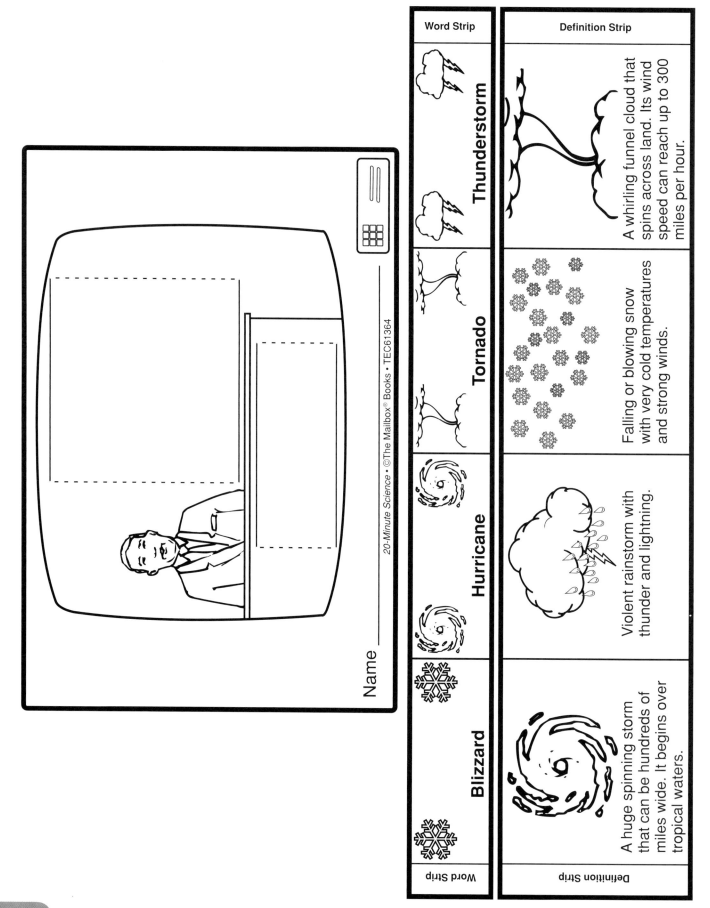

Name _____

Word Strip	Definition Strip
Thunderstorm	A whirling funnel cloud that spins across land. Its wind speed can reach up to 300 miles per hour.
Tornado	Falling or blowing snow with very cold temperatures and strong winds.
Hurricane	Violent rainstorm with thunder and lightning.
Blizzard	A huge spinning storm that can be hundreds of miles wide. It begins over tropical waters.

Word Strip

Definition Strip

Name _____

Cloud Journal

Keep a cloud journal for 5 days. Each day, draw the clouds and use the clues below to help you name them. Then guess what weather might be coming your way. An example has been done for you.

Cloud Clues

stratus	cumulus	cirrus
gray and gloomy	fair weather	fair weather
nimbostratus	cumulonimbus	cirrostratus
fog, rain, or snow	rain, thunder, and lightning	soon it will rain

Today is __Friday__.
I see __cumulus__
clouds.

I think tomorrow will be
__fair__.

Today is _____.
I see _____
clouds.

I think tomorrow will be
_____.

Today is _____.
I see _____
clouds.

I think tomorrow will be
_____.

Today is _____.
I see _____
clouds.

I think tomorrow will be
_____.

Today is _____.
I see _____
clouds.

I think tomorrow will be
_____.

Today is _____.
I see _____
clouds.

I think tomorrow will be
_____.

Objects in the Sky

From Day to Night

Materials:
flashlight
globe
small sticker

This simple demonstration helps students understand why we experience day and night. To begin, put the sticker on the globe to indicate where you live. Then place the globe on a table and dim the classroom lights. Have a volunteer shine the flashlight on the globe, illuminating your home (the sticker). Ask students if they think it is day or night where the sticker is located *(day)*. Turn the globe counterclockwise until the other side is illuminated. Lead students to realize that the sticker is now on the darker side of the globe, which indicates nighttime.

Why Do We Have Day and Night?

Caroline

Where Is the Sun?

Help students understand where the sun goes at night with this simple booklet project.

Materials for each student:
copy of page 110
6" yellow construction paper circle
three 6" white paper circles
access to a stapler

Steps for students:
1. Cut out the booklet backing and information cards.
2. Glue one card (numbers 1–3) to the bottom half of each white circle and the number 4 card to the bottom half of the booklet backing.
3. Read each card; then add an illustration in the space above the card.
4. Stack the white circles in order atop the booklet backing and put the yellow circle on top.
5. Staple the booklet at the top.
6. Title the booklet "Why Do We Have Day and Night?"

Earth & Space Science

Earth on the Move

Materials for each student:
copy of page 111

Day 1: Remind students that the earth's orbit around the sun creates the seasons. Explain that for several months each year, half of the earth is tilted toward the sun, receiving maximum sunlight (summer); the other half is tilted away, receiving minimal sunlight (winter). Then pair students and have each duo act out the earth's rotation and revolution around the sun. Have one student represent the sun, while the other student (earth) rotates counterclockwise and revolves counterclockwise around the sun. Have the students stop each quarter of the revolution to name a different season, making sure to say the names of the seasons in order.

Day 2: Review with students how and why the seasons change. Then have each child cut apart the banner sections on her copy of page 111. Have her glue banner page 3 to page 2 as shown. Direct each child to complete each sentence on her banner and then draw a picture to illustrate each sentence.

Solar Eclipse

Materials for each student:
plastic checker

Explain to students that a solar eclipse occurs when the moon's shadow passes over the earth. Use this experiment to demonstrate how the moon blocks the sun when this happens. Take students outside and direct them to stand 25 to 35 feet away from a tall tree or another large object. Have each child close her left eye and look at the tree with her right eye. Next, instruct each student to hold the checker in her right hand at arm's length, keep her left eye closed, and look at the tree. Then have her slowly bring the checker closer to her face until it is directly in front of her eye. Lead students in discussing what happens. *(As the checker gets closer to the child's eye, it begins to block her view of the tree until she can't see the tree at all, even though the checker is much smaller than the tree.)* Explain to students that just as the checker blocks the tree, the moon is able to block our view of the sun during a solar eclipse because the moon is closer to the earth than the sun is.

Earth & Space Science

By the Light of the Moon

Materials:
flashlight
plastic mirror
ball

Earth

Moon

To begin, ask students whether they think the moon produces its own light or the light comes from something else. Then ask three volunteers to each hold one of the materials. Dim the lights and instruct the child holding the flashlight (sun) to shine it so that the light reflects off the mirror (moon). Direct the student holding the ball (Earth) to position it so that it catches the light reflected off the moon. From this demonstration, lead students to realize that the light actually comes from the sun and is reflected off the surface of the moon.

Sun

The Phases of the Moon

Materials:
large, dark-colored ball, such as a basketball or kick ball, with an X drawn on one side
  (to remind students that the same side of the moon always faces the earth)
large flashlight

Steps:

1. Have one child hold a flashlight (sun). Have another child hold the ball (moon) up and away from his body so that the X is facing him and he is looking up a little to see the ball. Have the student with the flashlight stand a few feet in front of the child holding the ball and shine the light on the student holding the ball.
2. Dim the lights and point out that the moon is dark on the side that the child holding it sees. Explain to students that this is a *new moon*.
3. Have the student holding the ball slowly turn counterclockwise until he sees a small sliver of light on the ball. Inform students that this is a *crescent moon*.
4. Instruct the student to continue turning until he sees a little bit more of the ball illuminated. Explain to students that this is a *first-quarter moon*.
5. Direct the student to continue turning until all the side he can see is illuminated. Tell students this is a *full moon*.
6. Have the student keep turning. Point out that less and less of the ball will be illuminated. Have him stop when about three-fourths of the ball is dark. Inform students that this is the *third-quarter,* or *last-quarter moon*.
7. Instruct the student to keep turning until he sees another crescent moon and then a new moon.
8. Ask students whether the ball decreased in size as the student rotated. *(No.)* Then have your students explain what did change that made the moon appear to change shape. *(The amount of visible sunlight hitting the moon changed, making it only appear to change shape.)*

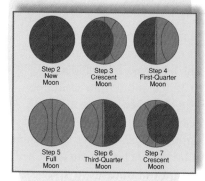

Step 2 New Moon	Step 3 Crescent Moon	Step 4 First-Quarter Moon
Step 5 Full Moon	Step 6 Third-Quarter Moon	Step 7 Crescent Moon

Earth & Space Science

Lunar Illusion

This partner experiment shows students how the moon fools us into thinking it is bigger than the stars.

Materials for each pair of students:
4" gray paper circle with a 2" circle cut from the center (give the pair both the frame and the circle cutout)

Steps:
1. Have one child in each duo hold the frame at arm's length in her line of vision. Direct her partner to stand five feet away and hold up the smaller circle (moon).
2. Instruct the partner with the frame to view the moon through the frame, noting its size.
3. Repeat the experiment, having the student with the moon stand 20 feet away.
4. Have the students in each pair switch roles and repeat the experiment.
5. Ask students how the size of the moon compared with the frame at 5 and 20 feet. Explain that the added distance made the moon only appear to get smaller. Then explain that in reality, the stars are much farther from the earth, which is the reason they appear much smaller.

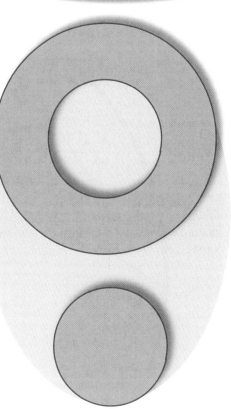

Exploring the Moon

Have students create these timelines to review the journey that helped improve our understanding of the moon.

Materials for each student:
copy of page 112
6" x 12" sheet of construction paper
6" black construction paper circle
5" white paper circle

Steps for students:
1. Decorate the white circle so that it looks like a moon. Glue it to the center of the black circle.
2. Cut out the strips on page 112.
3. Glue the black circle atop the construction paper so it is slightly overlapping it.
4. Put the strips in order by date. Glue the cards in order atop the construction paper. The first event should be at the bottom.
5. Starting at the bottom, read the cards in order to learn about the timeline of moon exploration.

Earth & Space Science

Booklet Backing and Information Cards

Use with "Where Is the Sun?" on page 106.

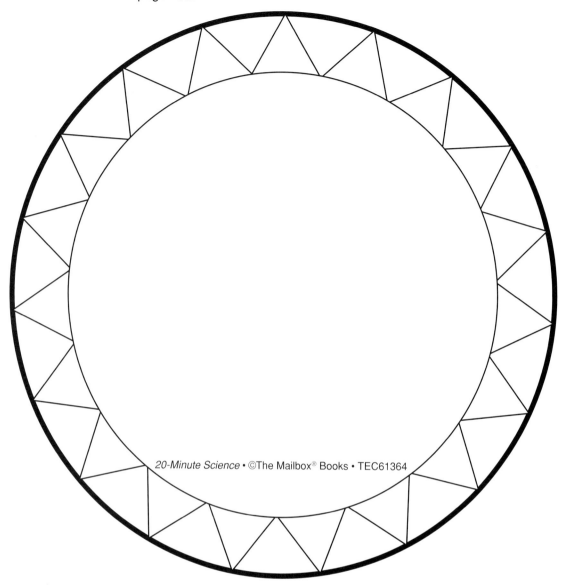

20-Minute Science • ©The Mailbox® Books • TEC61364

1. Earth rotates as it orbits the sun.	2. When the part of Earth that you live on is facing the sun, it is daytime where you live.
3. As the part of Earth that you live on rotates away from the sun, it becomes nighttime where you live.	4. It takes one year, or about 365 days, for Earth to complete its orbit around the sun.

Banner Section Patterns
Use with "Earth on the Move" on page 107.

Spring

In spring, I _____

_____

_____ . 1

20-Minute Science • ©The Mailbox® Books • TEC61364

Name

Summer

In summer, I _____

_____

_____ . 2

Fall

In fall, I _____

_____

_____ . 3

Glue to page 2.

Winter

In winter, I _____

_____

_____ . 4

111

Information Strips

Use with "Exploring the Moon" on page 109.

1687
Sir Isaac Newton explains the moon's motion
and its effect on Earth's tides.

TEC61364

1957
Soviet Union launches *Sputnik 1*.

1966
Soviet Union's *Luna 9* becomes the
first spacecraft to make a soft landing on
the moon.

1969
***Apollo 11* astronaut Neil Armstrong becomes**
the first man to walk on the moon.

1968
***Apollo 8* astronauts orbit the moon ten times.**

1609–1610
Galileo uses a telescope to study the moon.

Earth's Surface & Resources

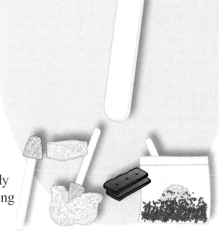

Inside the Earth

Materials for each student:
copy of page 117
large gumdrop
individually wrapped
   Rice Krispies Treats bar

2 sections of chocolate graham cracker
resealable plastic bag
craft stick

Day 1: Review the layers of the earth with students and share facts about the earth's layers. Then have each child complete a copy of page 117.

Day 2: To further reinforce understanding of the layers of the earth, have students follow the steps below to make Earth Pops.

Steps for each student:
1. Insert the craft stick into the center of the gumdrop (core).
2. Flatten the Rice Krispies Treats bar (mantle); then mold it around the gumdrop.
3. Put the graham cracker sections in the bag. Seal the bag and crush the crackers to make crumbs.
4. Place the Earth Pop in the bag with the crumbs and shake gently to evenly distribute the crumbs (crust). Press the crumbs on the pop before removing it from the bag.

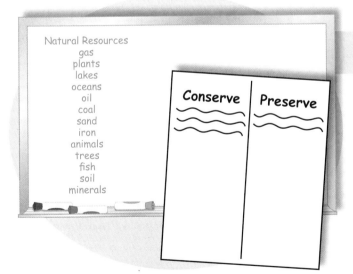

Natural Resources
    gas
    plants
    lakes
    oceans
    oil
    coal
    sand
    iron
    animals
    trees
    fish
    soil
    minerals

Conserve	Preserve

To Conserve or Preserve?

Materials:
chart paper labeled as shown

    Explain to students that *conservation* is the use of the earth's natural resources in a planned and careful way and *preservation* is keeping natural resources as safe and untouched as possible. Have students brainstorm natural resources as you list their ideas on the board. Then discuss with students which resources would benefit the environment by being conserved and which would benefit the environment by being preserved. Ask volunteers to write each resource listed on the board in the appropriate column on the chart.

Earth & Space Science

Conserving Energy

Materials:
chart paper
class supply of white paper

Discuss with students the importance of conserving the earth's energy. Then have students brainstorm ways energy is wasted at home and at school. List their ideas on chart paper. Instruct each student to use the list to write about conserving energy on his paper. Then have him add an illustration.

Turn off the light to save energy!

Down the Drain

Materials:
class supply of page 118
access to a sink
1-cup measuring cup
funnel
plastic pitchers or watering cans

Demonstrate for students the importance of water conservation with this simple experiment. Before lunch or snacktime, put a stopper in a sink and instruct each student to wash her hands at that sink. Later, use a measuring cup to scoop the water from the sink into the pitchers. Have the students count each cup of water as it is scooped from the sink. (Use the collected water to water classroom or outdoor plants.) Then have each student complete her copy of page 118 to record the results.

Earth & Space Science

Natural Heat

Materials:
3 tagboard squares (1 black, 1 white, and 1 green)
3 ice cubes
access to a warm, sunny location

Show your students the importance of color in creating solar energy with this fast-acting experiment. Place the squares in a sunny location and have students feel the squares as they begin to warm up. After a few minutes, put an ice cube on each square and have students observe which ice cube melts the quickest. *(The ice on the black square will melt first, while the ice on the white square will take the longest to melt.)* Explain to students that dark colors, like black, absorb most of the sun's heat, while light colors, like white, reflect most of the sun's heat. Other colors, like green, only absorb a small part of the sun's heat. Lead students to understand that this is why most items that use solar energy, like solar water heaters, are black.

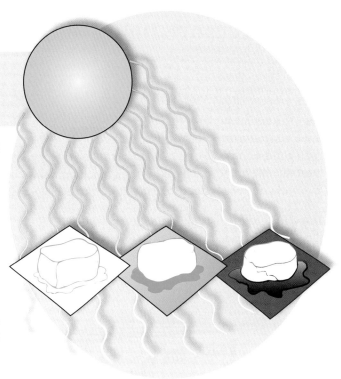

Made From Trees

Materials:
class supply of the leaf patterns on page 119 (make equal amounts of red, orange, green, and yellow leaves)
large tree cutout
supply of used magazines

Remind students that trees are a source of products that we use every day. Then divide the class into four groups, giving each group a different set of colored leaf patterns. Assign each group a different type of product: wood products for the green group, paper products for the red group, food products for the orange group, and other tree products (rubber, cork, etc.) for the yellow group. Have the members of each group glue magazine pictures or draw pictures of the tree products they have been assigned on their leaves. When each group is finished, display the leaves on the tree cutout under a title like the one shown. If desired, use one leaf of each color to provide a key for the display.

Earth & Space Science

Tree Treasure Hunt

Materials:
class supply of page 120
chart divided into three sections labeled "Wood," "Paper," and "Food"

Day 1: Remind students that tree products can be divided into three general categories: wood, paper, and food. Then give each child a copy of page 120. Instruct each child to take his reproducible home and have his family help him search for examples of tree products in each of the three categories.

Day 2: When the lists are returned, invite each child to share with the class the products he found. On the chart paper, record each different tree product identified.

Wood	Paper	Food
chair	cereal box	apple
table	paper towel	orange
stool	tissue paper	pecan
spoon	computer paper	walnut
TV stand	newspaper	peach
chest	magazine	pear

The Three Rs

Materials for each student:
assembled copy of the booklet on pages 121 and 122
access to a dictionary

To begin, discuss with students the differences between reducing, reusing, and recycling. Then have each child write her name on her booklet cover. For each booklet page, have each child read the word and write a definition of the word. (Have students use dictionaries if necessary.) Then have her draw a picture to show an example of each word.

Recycling to the Rescue

Materials for each student:
copy of page 123

To begin, remind students about the different kinds of recyclable materials—such as paper, glass, aluminum, and plastic—and the importance of separating them from nonrecyclable trash. Explain that recycling helps save the earth's natural resources. Then have each child complete his copy of page 123 to show his understanding of the different types of recyclables.

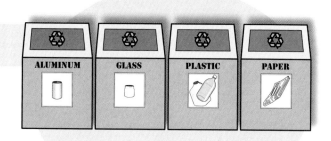

Earth & Space Science

Name _____

Inside the Earth

Use the clues below to help you label the earth.
Use the code on the moon to color each part of the earth.

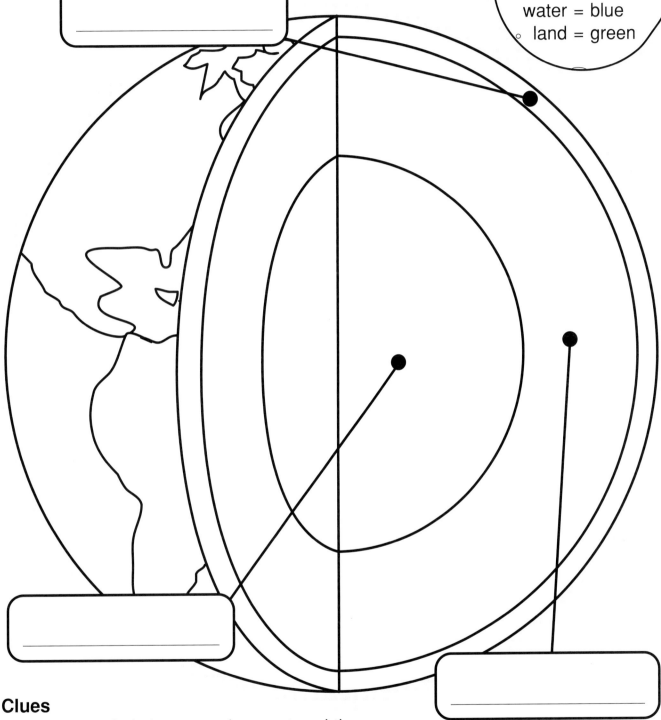

Color Code
crust = brown
mantle = orange
core = red
water = blue
land = green

Clues

1. The **mantle** is between the crust and the core.
2. We live on the outer layer called the **crust.**
3. The **core** is found in the center of the earth.

Careful Water User

Read the questions and then fill in the blanks below. Use a blue crayon to complete the water graph.

How many cups of water were used? _____

How many cups per student? _____

Some places and times I waste water:

1. _____

_____

2. _____

_____

3. _____

_____

Some ways I can save water:

1. _____

_____

2. _____

_____

3. _____

_____

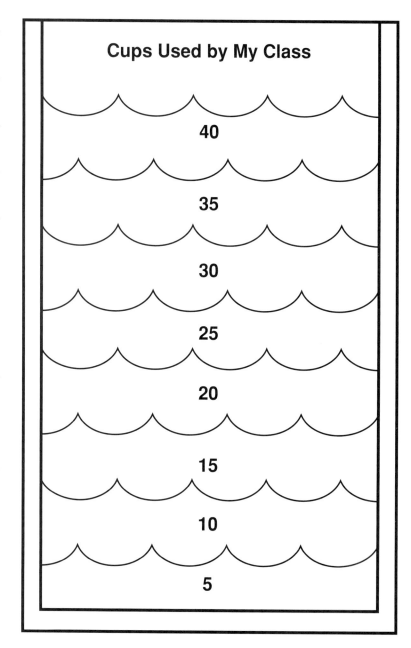

Cups Used by My Class

40

35

30

25

20

15

10

5

Note to the teacher: Use with "Down the Drain" on page 114.

Tree Treasure Hunt

Directions: Have an adult help you look around your home to find items that come from trees. As you search each room, try to find two or three food, paper, or wood products and list them in each treasure chest below.

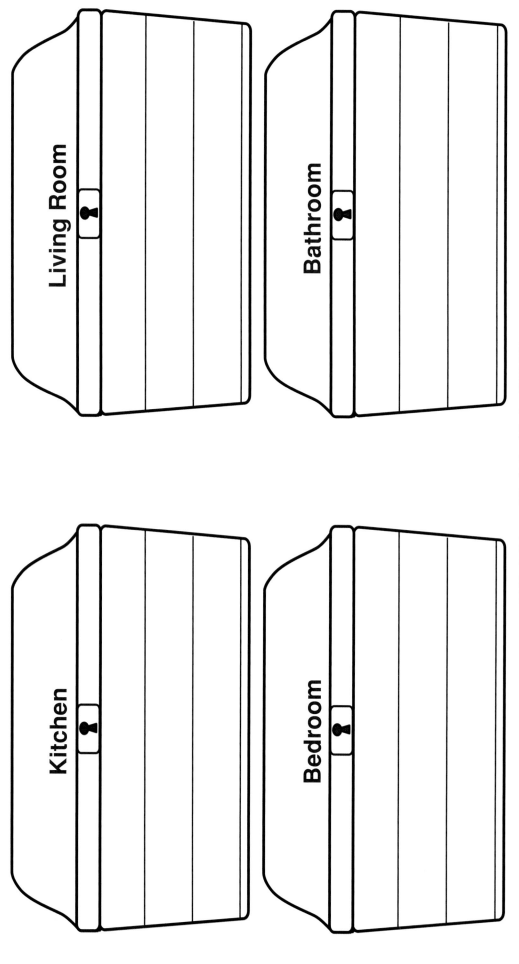

Kitchen

Living Room

Bedroom

Bathroom

20-Minute Science • ©The Mailbox® Books • TEC61364

Note to the teacher: Use with "Tree Treasure Hunt" on page 116.

Reduce, Reuse, and Recycle

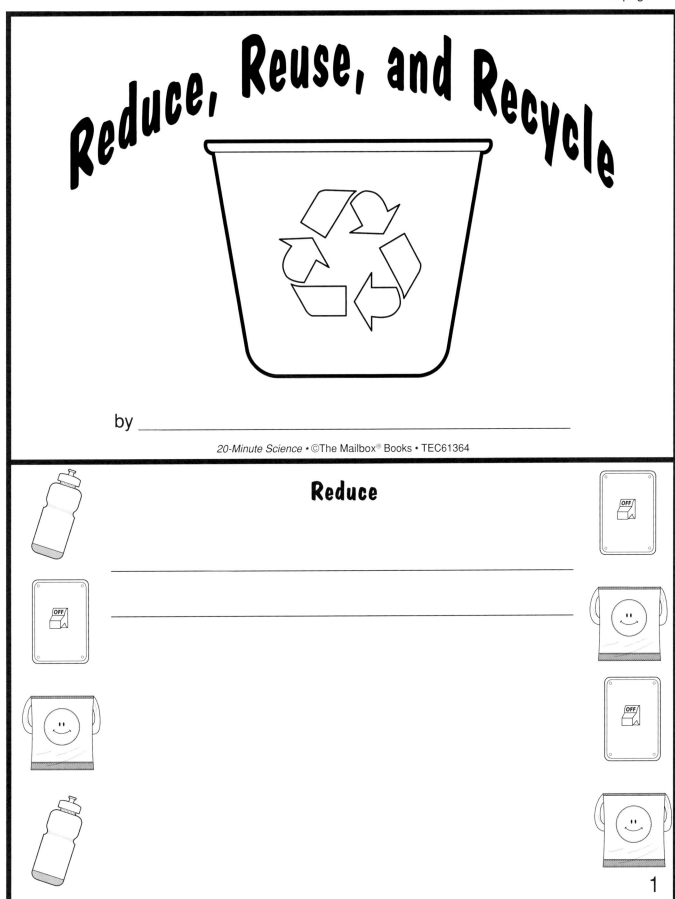

by _____

20-Minute Science • ©The Mailbox® Books • TEC61364

Reduce

_____

_____

1

Booklet Pages 2 and 3

Use with "The Three Rs" on page 116.

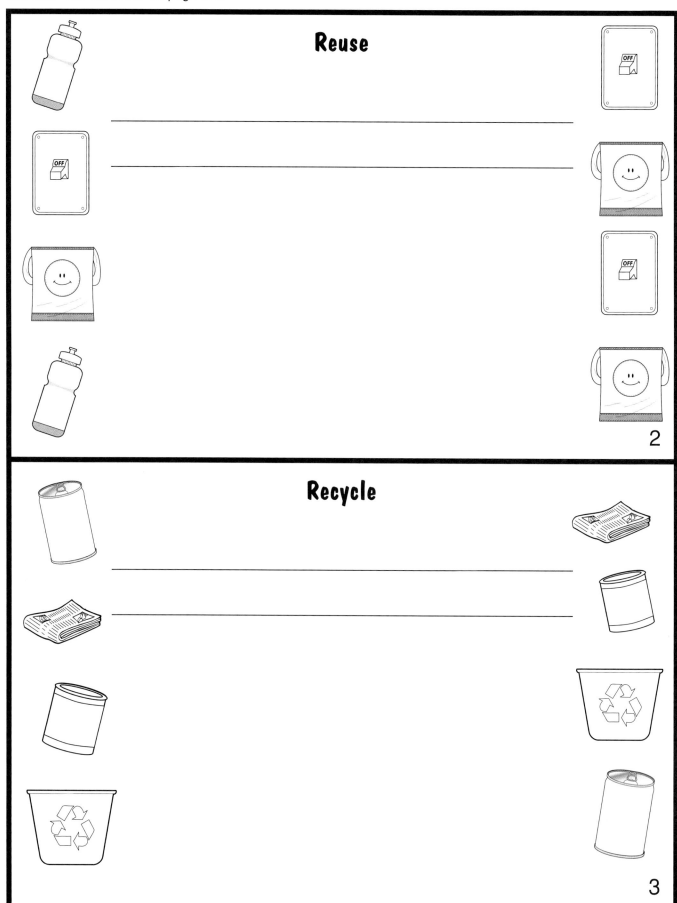

Reuse

2

Recycle

3

Putting Trash in Its Place

Cut out the cards.
Sort the cards by recycling material.
Glue each card onto the correct bin.

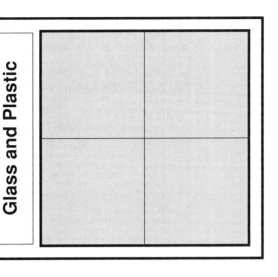

Glass and Plastic

Paper and Cardboard

Aluminum and Tin

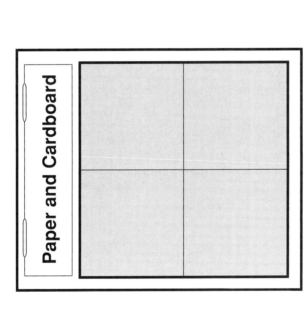

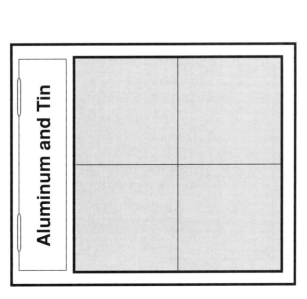

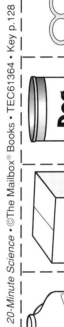

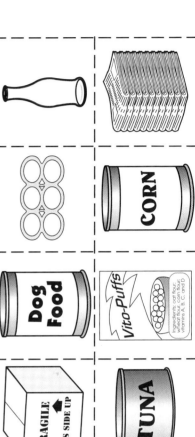

CORN

Dog
Food

Vito-Puffs

Ingredients: oat flour,
wheat flour, corn flour,
vitamins A, B, C, and D

FRAGILE
THIS SIDE UP

TUNA

MILK
1%

Mayonnaise

SOUP

20-Minute Science • ©The Mailbox® Books • TEC61364 • Key p.128

123

Note to the teacher: Use with "Recycling to the Rescue" on page 116.

Answer Keys

It Must Be a Mammal

		Does it have hair or fur?	Does it have a backbone?	Does it have two pairs of limbs?	Does it drink milk from its mother?
horse		X	X	X	X
grizzly bear		X	X	X	X
earthworm					
elephant		X	X	X	X
rabbit		X	X	X	X
spider		X			
kangaroo		X	X	X	X
chicken				X	X
grasshopper					
human		X	X	X	X

Bonus: Answers will vary.
earthworm—An earthworm has no limbs.
spider—A spider has more than two pairs of limbs.
chicken—A chicken hatches from an egg.
grasshopper—A grasshopper is an insect.

Page 13

Note: Some animals listed may live in more than one type of home.

	Wooded Area	Den	Nest	Burrow	Tunnel	Hollow Tree	Lodge
Bear		✓					
Porcupine				✓	✓	✓	
Skunk		✓		✓		✓	
Fox		✓		✓		✓	
Squirrel			✓			✓	
Chipmunk				✓	✓		
Rabbit				✓	✓		
Marmot				✓			
Woodchuck		✓		✓	✓		
Mole				✓	✓		
Mouse	✓		✓	✓		✓	
Deer	✓						
Beaver							✓
Opossum		✓				✓	
Raccoon	✓	✓				✓	
Marten						✓	
Otter		✓		✓			
Muskrat				✓			

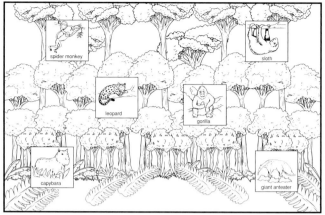

Bonus: Answers will vary.

Page 19

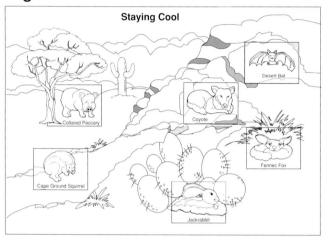

Page 20

Cetaceans
The two types of cetaceans are **toothed whales** and **baleen whales**.
Baleen whales do not have **teeth**.
Toothed whales use **echolocation** to find their food.

Sirenians
The two types of sirenians are **manatees** and **dugongs**.
Manatees are sometimes called **sea cows**.

Pinnipeds
Three types of pinnipeds are **seals**, **sea lions**, and **walruses**.
The name *pinniped* comes from Latin words meaning **fin-footed**.

Sea Otters
Sea otters do not have a layer of **blubber**.
Sea otters stay warm because of their **thick fur**.

Page 21

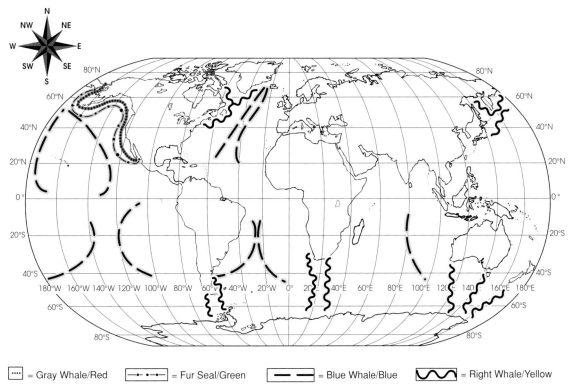

⌐....⌐ = Gray Whale/Red   ⌐—·—·—⌐ = Fur Seal/Green   ⌐—— ——⌐ = Blue Whale/Blue   ⌐〰〰⌐ = Right Whale/Yellow

Page 22

1. walrus
2. dugong
3. killer whale
4. 21 feet
5. sea otter, dugong, walrus, killer whale

Page 31

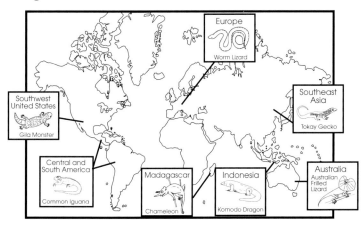

Page 37

Insects:

horsefly	cotton boll moth
praying mantis	head louse
goliath beetle	walkingstick
swallowtail butterfly	mosquito
stinkbug	monarch butterfly
cat flea	fruit fly
crane fly	giant water bug
rove beetle	stag beetle
biddy dragonfly	snakefly
aphid	army ants
leaf insect	water boatman
fire ant	

Noninsects:

tick	crab spider
harvestman	scorpion
black widow spider	tarantula
centipede	

Page 40

A ladybug lays eggs on the bottom of a leaf.	Larvae hatch out of the eggs and begin to eat aphids.	Each larva grows bigger and sheds its skin.	A larva attaches itself under a leaf and sheds its skin once more. Now it is called a pupa.	A few days later, a ladybug emerges from the cocoon.
1	2	3	4	5

Page 41

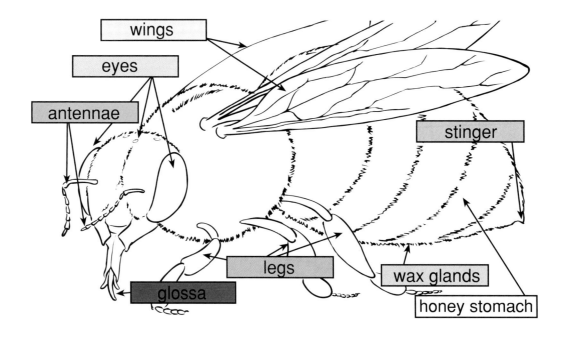

Page 42

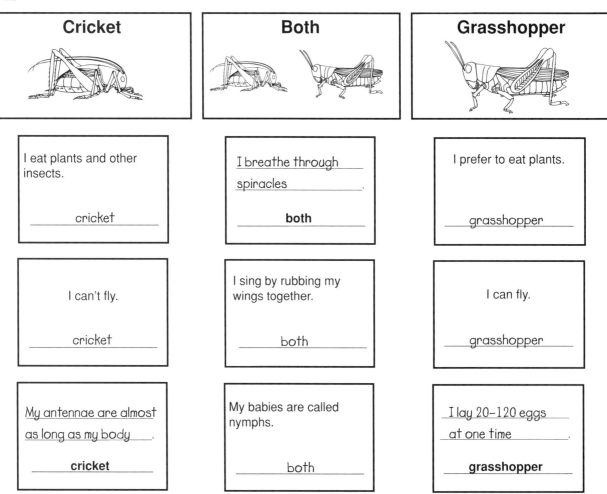

Page 53

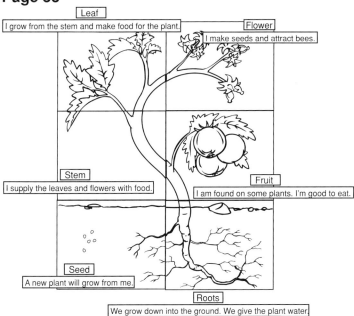

Leaf
I grow from the stem and make food for the plant.

Flower
I make seeds and attract bees.

Stem
I supply the leaves and flowers with food.

Fruit
I am found on some plants. I'm good to eat.

Seed
A new plant will grow from me.

Roots
We grow down into the ground. We give the plant water.

Page 54

Order will vary.
A1, B1, C1: radish, carrot, beet
A2, B2, C2: peas, beans, nuts
A3, B3, C3: lettuce, spinach, cabbage
A4, B4, C4: apple, pear, peach
D1, D2: celery stalk, asparagus
D3, D4: broccoli floret, cauliflower head

Page 55

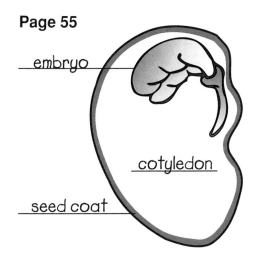

embryo

cotyledon

seed coat

Page 59

1. desert
2. mountain
3. tropics
4. grassland
5. seashore
6. waterside

Bonus: Answers will vary.

Page 69

Wind Instruments:
Flute
Trumpet
Clarinet
Tuba

Percussion Instruments:
Snare Drum
Cymbals
Kettledrum
Triangle

Stringed Instruments:
Guitar
Harp
Violin
String Bass

Page 76

Answers will vary.
1. There are changes in size and shape.
   Yes.
   It is a physical change.
2. There are changes in size, shape, color, texture, and substance.
   No.
   It is a chemical change.
3. There are changes in size and shape.
   Yes.
   It is a physical change.
4. There are changes in color and substance.
   No.
   It is a chemical change.
5. There are changes in color.
   Yes.
   It is a physical change.

Page 87

1. Igneous rock forms when magma cools and hardens.
2. Basalt is the most common igneous rock.
3. Sedimentary rock forms from layers of sediment.
4. Sandstone is one type of sedimentary rock.
5. Metamorphic rock forms when rocks are changed by heat and/or pressure.
6. Marble is a type of metamorphic rock.

Pages 88 and 89

Igneous Rock—This type of rock forms when molten material, or magma, cools and hardens.

Metamorphic Rock—This type of rock forms when heat or pressure or both cause changes in the other two types of rock.

Sedimentary Rock—This type of rock forms when small pieces of clay, silt, or sand settle into layers on the bottoms of lakes and oceans. The pressure of the water and the layers above compress the pieces into rock.

Page 90

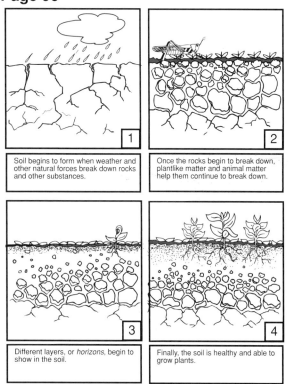

1. Soil begins to form when weather and other natural forces break down rocks and other substances.

2. Once the rocks begin to break down, plantlike matter and animal matter help them continue to break down.

3. Different layers, or *horizons*, begin to show in the soil.

4. Finally, the soil is healthy and able to grow plants.

Page 91

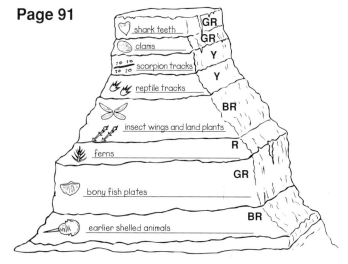

GR — shark teeth
GR — clams
Y — scorpion tracks
Y — reptile tracks
BR — insect wings and land plants
R — ferns
GR — bony fish plates
BR — earlier shelled animals

Page 102

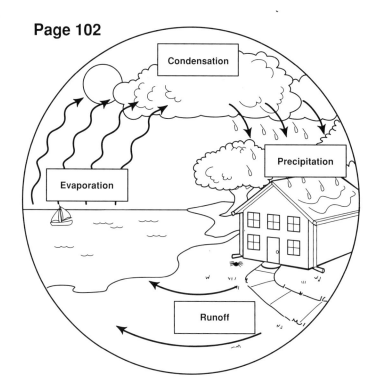

Condensation
Precipitation
Evaporation
Runoff

Page 117

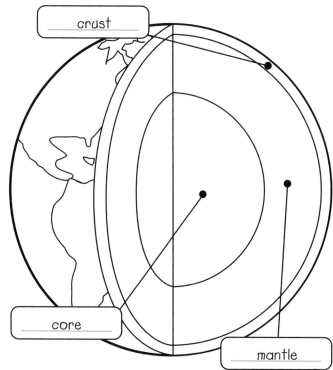

crust
core
mantle

Page 123

Order may vary.

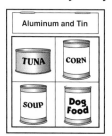

Aluminum and Tin
TUNA   CORN
SOUP   Dog Food

Paper and Cardboard
Vita-Puffs
FRAGILE THIS SIDE UP

Glass and Plastic
Mayonnaise   MILK 1%